VIDEO

JOHN HEDGECOE

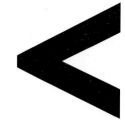

VIDEO

JOHN HEDGECOE

MITCHELL
BEAZLEY

VIDEO: A COMPLETE INTRODUCTORY GUIDE

First published in 1989 as Hedgecoe On Video by Pyramid,
  an imprint of Octopus Books Limited
Published in paperback in 1991 by Hamlyn Publishing Group Limited
Reprinted in 1991 and 1993

This edition, fully revised and updated, published in 1995 by
Mitchell Beazley, an imprint of Reed Consumer Books Limited,
Michelin House, 81 Fulham Road, London SW3 6RB,
and Auckland, Melbourne, Singapore and Toronto

Additional text for, and Editor of, 1995 edition: Chris George
Research Assistant: Jenny Mackintosh

Executive Editor: Sarah Polden
Art Editor: Vivienne Brar
Co-ordinating Editor: Anthea Snow
Design: John Grain, Louise Griffiths
Production: Juliette Butler
Illustrations: Mei Lim, Jim Robins, Chris Forsey, Bob Reed,
  Tony Hannaford

Additional text for 1989 edition: James McCarter, Philip Wilkinson
Editors for 1989 edition: Philip Wilkinson, John Stace

A CIP catalogue record for this book is available from
the British Library.

ISBN 1 85732 719 5

Produced by Mandarin Offset
Printed and bound in Malaysia

Contents

Foreword

I first picked up a video camera about fifteen years ago. Compared with the compact camcorders available today, it was a cumbersome thing, with a separate portable recorder pack that weighed heavily on the shoulder. Nevertheless, I was hooked. The instant replay of friends and family on the television screen made me realize the great flexibility offered by the medium.

The first thing that struck me was that many of the techniques I'd perfected in still photography applied to the video, but there were many others that didn't. The big difference was that you had to think of time and action as well as of the more static concepts of composition and lighting.

The technology has come a long way since then, and millions of people have discovered the creative freedom that video offers. Image quality has improved dramatically, and colour rendition is now as good as that available with film. Automatic functions make the camcorder simplicity itself to operate – in most situations you can simply switch on and shoot, not bothering about technicalities such as exposure levels and focusing requirements.

Although most enthusiasts begin with tapes of their family life, there really is no limit to the material you can record. Documentary issues, sports, travelogues and dramas are all accessible.

This book is designed as a guide to acquiring those video skills which are needed to capture best a subject on videotape. It deals with technical points where necessary, but the emphasis is placed on an artistic, visual understanding of the discipline. More than anything else, good video is dependent on forward planning: planning both what you intend to shoot and how you want each shot to look.

One final word: videotape is cheap and reusable, so don't hesitate to experiment with your shots. If you suddenly think 'I wonder what it would look like if . . .', try it and see. There really are no rules in video, only guidelines. I hope the guidelines I've put down in this book will add to your enjoyment and understanding of an exciting and satisfying form of communication.

JOHN HEDGECOE

Introduction

If anything characterizes the twentieth century, it is the proliferation of images. First came the silent movies, followed by 'talkies' in the late 1920s. At about the same time television was being developed. In the 1950s and 60s, television became almost universal. In the 70s and 80s came home video. Today, the average person watches as much as three to four hours of television each day – an occupation that takes up more time than anything else but sleep and work.

The result is that we have all become used to watching moving images on the screen. We have absorbed the techniques used by programme makers to such an extent that they are second nature to us. We understand about close-ups and cuts from one shot to another. We instinctively know when time is supposed to have passed. We know when we are looking at the same view as the main character.

One of the unspoken conventions is that what we see on the screen is, for want of a better word, 'reality'. Of course, it is anything but that. That documentary shot of people living in a high-rise flat was only achieved by using an army of researchers and technicians. A great deal of time and effort is spent by professional programme makers in hiding this fact.

Time is another quality that is frequently manipulated. A videotape which runs as long as the actual events that it depicts would appear interminable. We are used to whole days' or weeks' events being condensed into half an hour's screen time.

When it comes to making your own videos, you will probably feel an initial sense of disappointment in that your images don't look like those you're used to seeing each night on the television. This may be partly due to basic deficiencies of technique, such as keeping the camera steady, which can be readily overcome with perseverance. But it will also be because you haven't followed the accepted practices that the professionals use, many of which can only be achieved in the editing process.

However, it is easy to be daunted when thinking of the enormous resources available to professional television crews. But this would be to forget the importance of the fundamental techniques that go into programme making. First and foremost are basic research and observation. Any time spent researching a project will not be wasted. The more you know about your subject, the richer and more compelling your coverage will be.

Secondly comes a strong visual sense. People who have worked in stills photography will have gradually acquired the sense of looking at the

8

Above and left: In the heyday of Hollywood directors created elaborate visual effects. But the early film makers' attention to detail provides a vital lesson for the modern video director. Good video takes time – in preparation, setting up the shots, and editing it all together at the end of the shoot.

world through a viewfinder, of observing a scene selectively. The technique holds good with video – provided the need for action is remembered. Two people could shoot in exactly the same environment, but the one with the best observational and compositional sense will produce the most interesting images.

Perhaps the third requirement is an organizational ability that would be appreciated in a works manager. You need to be able to simultaneously conceive of a project in its broad terms and remember detail. Will you be able to use lights when you intend to shoot indoors? Did you remember to pack spare batteries? Do you know exactly how long it is going to take you to get from location A to location B?

Finally, successful video is all about timing. Everything that you record is worth a certain amount of time, and no more. Exactly how much time is a matter of judgement, depending both on the subject and on the intended audience. Even the most devoted grandparents may become a little restless after two hours of baby's first tottering steps have passed on the screen.

In general, think of which aspects of the action you are recording and give them an according amount of screen time. Most shots need not be shown on screen for more than ten seconds. This is enough time for the audience to assimilate what

Above and right:
Although the equipment looks antiquated, the early television studio contained the same elements as a modern video studio set-up: a close-knit team responsible for camera, sound, lights, props and direction.

Above: Many of the latest camcorder designs have large built-in colour screens, the primary purpose of which is for replaying your footage when you are away from home. But they can be used when shooting too. Whatever type of camcorder you use, you need to be totally familiar with how it works if you are going to be able to concentrate on getting the coverage you want.

is being presented on the screen. For informal family events, a running time of about thirty minutes is usually quite long enough.

Within the main body of this book are a number of video projects of progressive complexity. After a overview of video equipment and basic techniques and a discussion of the tricks of the trade, the first project tackled is a wedding, something everyone with a video camera will be called on to record sooner or later. Next comes a chapter on recording individuals in different contexts, followed by coverage of a family holiday. A documentary feature follows, based on a day in the life of a small convent. Sports coverage comes next, then a chapter which looks at techniques for creating tension and suspense in dramas.

The final chapters look at the expanded possibilities available if you can work with a larger crew and greater facilities, and at the central importance of editing, with the additional choice of incorporating basic special effects and graphics facilities offered by today's computers.

Because the image is so important in our society – for informing, explaining, selling and a host of other functions – working with video can begin with home movies and graduate to a whole range of activities. Many amateurs move on to become semi-professionals, recording weddings, or creating promotional material for their companies. The opportunities are everywhere: the school play or sports day, local sports and social clubs – most will be happy to allow you to turn up and record.

Since you are not going to be paid for your services, you can use these occasions to experiment. If the experiments don't work, no one loses out. With experiment comes technical competence and growing confidence. There really is no limit to what you can do with video once you start to master the creative techniques and begin to get access to greater facilities.

Video Basics

Although it is artistic skill that makes a good video, it is still necessary to have some technical knowledge about how video works. For a start, the camcorder user must have a good idea of what today's cameras are capable of, and the situations where the results on screen might not meet your expectations.

This chapter, then, not only gives you a broad view of how a modern camcorder works, it also shows some of the technical skills that you need to be acquainted with if you are going to get the most out of your equipment.

1: To be effective, a still shot relies on the photographer capturing a particular moment which typifies the subject. The action is frozen in the frame, but the viewer can readily imagine what follows. Techniques of selecting the correct exposure and lens speed, and choosing how to frame the shot, are used by the photographer to achieve a clear image and a sense of immediacy.

Moving Pictures

It is worth stressing right at the beginning that although video and still photography have certain points in common, the differences are so great that the two approaches must be regarded as separate disciplines. But while certain visual skills learned in still photography will be of great use when making a video, there will be many new techniques to master. Another important point to note is that when you look at the photographs in this book you must try to see them as instants captured from a sequence of rapidly moving pictures, for, in video, time is rarely frozen.

Video audiences are interested first and foremost in what is happening now, and in what will happen next. Therefore the first key lesson in mastering video techniques is appreciating that videos tell a story, even if it is merely how clouds move and change shape. You must also appreciate that when composing a video shot, you are doing so not just in terms of two-dimensional space, as in stills photography, but in time and volume, using the camera to move around the subject. To an extent, the subject is therefore the action which unfolds in the space in front of your viewfinder.

In the quest to make interesting, creative and satisfying home movies, ranging from straightforward records of family events to more sophisticated mini-dramas and documentaries, you can improve your video skills considerably if you watch television critically. This doesn't mean deciding whether a programme is good or bad. It means thinking about the camera position and angle of each shot, noticing when the shot changes and how the change is accomplished. Ask yourself what a scene might look like if shot from a different angle, or what would be the effect if the main character was shown in close-up rather than from a distance?

The chapters in this book tackle eight projects designed to explain the creative and organizational techniques vital to video success. They cover everyday situations which most camcorder owners will want to tackle, from a wedding and family holiday, to more ambitious ideas, such as scripting and recording a drama.

Since first videos are often disappointing you may conclude that without the huge budgets and technical resources of the professionals you have little chance of producing a tape that can compare with what you see on television. But if you plan carefully and work within your limitations, you will be surprised at the polish you can attain.

The first hurdle
Although home editing facilities are getting easier to use, and cheaper, all the time, for many people the thought of having to spend time and money on this post-production stage can be off-putting. If this is the case, you may have to edit as you shoot – known as 'in-camera editing' – which will have a major bearing on the way in which you approach your subject. Home editing can be done with a minimum of equipment – and this book will show you how – but the projects have been so designed that you can use in-camera editing if preferred.

And finally, try to use your camera as much as possible. Experimentation and innovation are at the heart of this exciting and accessible new medium. The more different subjects you tackle, the more you will become proficient in the huge range of cinematic techniques.

2–4: These are a few shots from a short video sequence of the little girl eating the ice cream. She does not have to pose or wait for the shot to be framed, so her movements tend to be more natural. Using the zoom lens, the cameraperson can move in closer to catch her in close-up. The short sequence gets its interest from what the girl is doing – that is, from the action on the screen.

1: This simple holiday sequence of people eating a meal shows how the family snapshot can be translated into video terms. The first shot shows them around the table. It includes some information about the room, so that we can see where they are, but there is not very much action.

2: Zooming in on part of the table gives the sequence more dynamism – but don't be tempted to overuse the zoom in this way. It is usually better to stop recording, zoom in, then start recording again.

3: Shots like this may seem unremarkable as stills, but the action – father helping himself while the child takes a drink – gives movement to the video.

1–3: These shots from a rock video show a different problem. One member of the band is hidden from the camera. By 'crabbing' round the group whilst recording we show each of the musicians clearly. This type of camera movement makes for more dynamic footage.

Video and Film

Unlike film, video is an electronic medium. Light is focused by the lens onto a light-sensitive device known as a CCD (charge coupled device). This is the heart of the video camera, and is made up of hundreds of thousands of cells called pixels. Each pixel translates the light that falls on it into an electric current – the more light, the more current.

These electrical signals travel to the recording section of the camcorder – a miniaturized version of the domestic VCR. The current creates a small magnetic field which is recorded on the magnetic coating of the tape. To view the image, the process is reversed: the magnetic field on the tape creates an electric current which is used to generate the picture in the viewfinder, or on the television.

The great advantage of video tape over film is that it is an instant process. As soon as you have recorded something you can play it back again, even if you are away from a TV screen – thanks to the miniature monitors that are built into most camcorders. There is no need to wait a fortnight for the film to come back from the laboratory; and there's no need for a projector as the camcorder itself is the playback machine. What's more video tape is re-usable. Make a mistake, and you can re-record over the tape. The batteries are also rechargeable – so after the initial cost of buying a camcorder, the running costs can be very low.

Another advantage of video cameras is that they will record in very low light. This is because a weak electrical current generated by the CCD can be electronically boosted by the automatic gain control, or AGC. Additional lighting is rarely essential – though this may improve the overall quality of the picture, when the grain introduced by the AGC is unwanted. A camcorder, therefore, is quite capable of recording by candlelight.

Although many of the techniques used in video making are the same as those used in film, when it comes to editing the mechanics are totally different. Editing film is a straightforward mechanical process – you cut out the frames you want, and splice them together in the finished order. With video this is not possible. The frames on the tape are not visible. They are recorded as magnetic patterns laid out in very thin, diagonal stripes across the surface of the tape (this allows as much information as possible about each frame to be recorded on the narrow tape).

To edit video tape, the sections that you want have to be re-recorded from one tape to another in the order you require them. Essentially this is a simple matter of connecting a cable between your camcorder and a VCR. The camcorder plays the original tape, whilst the VCR is set to record at the appropriate sections.

White-balance window: Your camcorder needs to take readings to find out the type of light you are recording under and correct the colours so that they will appear natural on screen.

Microphone: Don't forget that all camcorders record sound as well as pictures. Many record in stereo, although you'll need a suitable TV, or you'll have to hook up your camcorder through your hi-fi, to hear the results.

Lens: Practically all camcorders have built-in zoom lenses offering you the chance to get in really close to faraway objects. Wide-angle performance, however, is much more variable, and this is worth checking when buying, otherwise you'll have problems shooting in small rooms, or when faced with a sweeping panorama.

Zoom rocker: The power zoom control is found on the right-hand side of the camera above the record/pause button. Its main use is for framing up shots before shooting, not for use whilst recording.

Electronic viewfinder: this miniature TV not only lets you see what you are shooting, but it is also used for framing up shots before recording, and gives on-screen information on the functions you are currently using, and a counter reading. It also allows you to replay your footage whilst you are away from your TV set. Some camcorders have colour viewfinder, but many are black and white.

Creative controls: The number of creative functions you will find varies enormously from camera to camera. Some are very useful, whilst others are no more than worthless gizmos. Features worth considering include image stabilizers, faders, wipes, edit functions and titlers.

Secret panels: Less used buttons are usually hidden behind panels, so they don't clutter up the outside of the camera when not used. Connection sockets for linking up your camcorder to a TV or VCR will usually be covered up too.

Exposure controls: The amount of manual control you have over exposure will vary enormously from model to model. Some will give you none, whilst others will give you the opportunity to change shutter, iris and gain controls. All camcorders will have automatic settings.

Camcorder Functions

Home video making began in the late 1970s with the arrival of 'portable' equipment. However, by today's standards it was far from easy to carry around, as the camera and recorder were two separate units. A heavy tape deck was carried on a strap that bit into one shoulder, whilst a cumbersome camera was supported on the other. The two units were connected by a cable that seemed to conspire to make shooting even more awkward than it already was.

The big step forward was made in 1983 with the introduction of the first all-in-one units. The camcorder (literally a CAMera and reCORDER in a single casing) was born. These were much easier to use, although they were still large and heavy, and so had to be supported on the shoulder. Since then camcorders have become progressively smaller and lighter. Today many camcorders are small enough to be held neatly in the palm of your hand.

The miniaturization of video cameras, and the search for better picture quality, has led to a number of different video tape formats – each with its different advantages and limitations (which are discussed on page 25).

The great advantage of today's palm-sized camcorders is that they are far more portable and less obtrusive than their predecessors. This not only makes them more convenient, it also means that you are less likely to be put off by the idea of taking a camcorder out and about with you. There is a disadvantage, though. The lighter the camera, the more difficult it is to hold it steady – particularly when using the telephoto end of the zoom. For this reason, professional video cameras are still supported on the shoulder – and don't have to be held with the arms alone in front of the eye. Image stabilizers, however, are appearing on more and more domestic camcorders, and these do an impressive job of beating the shakes even when using the highest magnifications of your lens.

Choosing a camcorder

If your interest is in shooting family videos, where it is vital to have the camera ready at all times to film unpredictable and spontaneous family scenes, a lightweight camera that you can carry around easily is probably the best option. If you are more interested in subjects like drama, where you will plan everything meticulously and set up the shots, then there is no reason why you shouldn't pick a larger model. In any case, the size of camcorder will be partly determined by which tape format you prefer, and which camera features you want.

Whatever you write on your shopping list, it is essential that you try out a camcorder before you buy it. The size of the camera is likely to have a direct relationship to the size of the controls. If you have large hands, small buttons may be difficult to use. Try and find one that fits your hand well, where you can reach the major controls, such as zoom rocker, record button and manual focus, easily. The less-used buttons must not be so small your fingers can't operate them.

Check also that you can hold the camera steady for several minutes (with the battery fitted) with the viewfinder to your eye. With patience, you should find something that you are happy with. Unlike stills cameras, the design of camcorders varies a lot from model to model, because, as the signals are passed around electronically, the way the components are laid out behind the lens is not important.

Left-handed people may have particular trouble in finding a model that feels comfortable. Nearly all camcorders are designed to be strapped to your right hand, with the primary controls being activated with your right thumb and forefinger. Remember that no store stocks all the camcorders on the market, so shop around until you find something that you are completely satisfied with. There are lots of video magazines devoted to how to buy and use camcorders – and these are a good way to familiarize yourself with prices and current features before you head off to the high street or shopping mall.

Sophistication or simplicity?

The table on page 24 shows the features you can expect to find on most camcorders. Top of the range models will have many more besides, to add creative touches to a production, or to give you more control over the automatic functions. Simpler models, on the other hand, may not be fitted with fairly useful features such as manual focus or backlight compensation.

It may be tempting to choose the camera with the least buttons, because you assume that it is the simplest to use. You should remember though that practically every camera can be set completely to automatic – with autofocus, auto exposure, and autocolour correction. So even the most sophisticated cameras are easy to use – you just have to ignore most of the buttons. If you buy a simpler camera, you may become frustrated a few months down the line by the lack of creative controls.

Camcorder controls are normally divided into two sections. There are those to operate the tape deck during replay, and those that control the video signal and the light entering the camera. The key to good camerawork is to know what each of the controls does and where each can be found, without a second thought. So invest a few hours in reading the instruction manual carefully, and trying out each control in turn, before you start recording your first video masterpiece.

Zoom lenses

Virtually all camcorder have a zoom lens, with zoom ratios (the difference in magnification of the image between the telephoto and wide-angle ends of the lens) ranging from 3:1 to 15:1 (or 3x to 15x). Some cameras even have electronic zooms where the telephoto settings can be digitally enlarged to give you effective zoom ratios of up to 100x (100:1).

It is easy to be tempted by cameras with the more powerful zooms, which allow you to close in on the action without you having to move any closer. But all camcorders, even those with only 6x zooms, have a very powerful telephoto setting when compared to the average stills camera. Most are quite capable of covering a sports match from the sidelines, or wildlife at a fair distance.

However, it is the wide-angle setting that is, perhaps, more important. The angle of view on the widest zoom setting of different camcorders can vary enormously. There are times when you just can't move back any further to fit the subject into the frame – such as shooting the family around the house, or when videoing the outside of a large building. It is here that the wider lens settings come into their own. Interchangeable lenses are normally only found on professional video cameras, though one or two top-end hobbyist cameras have been launched with this useful facility.

You will find many references to the use of the zoom control throughout this book. It can be used in many ways but the cardinal rule is not to overuse the zoom whilst you are actually recording. The main use of the zoom is to frame up your shots before you press the record button – so that you get the subject exactly the size that you want it, and then commit the shot to tape. If you want to move in closer, it is best to stop recording, zoom in and change camera angle – and only then start recording again.

Microphones

It is important to remember that video cameras record sound as well as pictures. You can easily get carried away with the picture, and ignore the sounds that you are also trying to capture on tape. All camcorders come with a built-in microphone, but this has limitations that are different from those imposed by the video side of the camera. For a start, sound, unlike light, does not travel well over distances. So a telephoto shot of a person standing on the other side of the street may look great, but you won't hear what they are saying. These microphones are designed to pick up sound mainly to the front of the camera, but they will also pick up some sound from the sides and the rear too – including the user's breathing and the whine of the tape transport motor.

For this reason it is a good idea to buy a camcorder that has sockets for plugging in headphones and additional microphones. A headset will tell you exactly what sound you are recording – rather than you assuming the microphone can hear exactly what you are hearing. A mic socket, on the other hand, will allow you to pick a specialist microphone that is better suited to the particular job in hand; and will enable you to move the microphone away from the camera and nearer the subject, when necessary.

Viewfinders

Most people are shocked to find that many camcorders still have black-and-white viewfinders. After all, every camcorder records in colour. The reason for this is because black-and-white monitors provide a more detailed small-screen image than a colour one. This is better for manual focusing, for instance.

Colour screens are becoming increasingly popular, however. These use LCD technology to get a colour TV that is small enough to fit onto a camcorder. A colour display comes into its own when shooting sport, where a black-and-white picture would make telling the two teams apart a nightmare, or when filming wildlife, where your subject may merge into the background, thanks to its camouflage from predators.

Big colour built-in screens are also found on more and more cameras. These have the advantage that two or three people can watch a video that you have just shot. With smaller viewfinders, you can only watch one at a time.

It is important to realize that a viewfinder does not only show you the picture you are recording. For a start, it will also show you what the camcorder is pointing at when you are in pause mode. The difference between these two modes must be learnt very early on – unless you'll think you are recording an important event, when in fact you are in pause. The thing to look out for is the wording in the viewfinder itself – usually displayed in the top right-hand corner.

The viewfinder will also tell you other pieces of important information about what the camcorder is doing. It will, for example, give you a readout of the tape counter numbers, it will tell you when your battery is about to run out, and will tell you when you have a particular function or exposure mode switched on. You must learn to continuously scan this information as you shoot – don't get mesmerized by the events and subjects that you are recording.

Below: The viewfinders on most camcorders can be angled to provide a comfortable shooting position, or for when you want to shoot from waist height.

Above: The main weight of the camcorder is supported with a wrist strap on the right-hand side of the camcorder. This should be sufficiently tightened using the Velcro fastener to ensure that it is held steady against the hand. The thumb and forefinger of the right hand are then generally used to control the record button and the motorized zoom rocker respectively.

Above: Although the right hand takes most of the weight, the left hand should also be used to give extra support. This should be cradled underneath the front of the camera in such a way so that you can reach the manual focus controls when necessary.

Above: Most camcorders have built-in zooms, which often means you have to compromise on wide-angle performance for the sake of a powerful telephoto setting. Some cameras, like the one pictured, however, have interchangeable lenses. This means you can use specialist wide-angle zooms, or extremely powerful telephotos, for particular tasks.

Below: Camcorders with built-in screens are ideal for watching what you have just shot when you are away from home.

FUNCTIONS

USES

Auto exposure

Every camcorder on the market nowadays will adjust itself automatically to give the right exposure in a wide range of light levels – from a candlelit room to a sun-drenched beach. The main way that light is controlled is by the iris, an adjustable aperture in the lens itself that opens or closes. This copes with most situations. But in lowlight, a further control is needed. To boost the picture brightness, the AGC (automatic gain control) amplifies the current from the CCD chip.

Automatic exposure works well in most situations, can have problems in high contrast lighting, such as when a subject is backlit, or when shooting street lights at night. Here some form of manual exposure override is useful – the most basic of which is a backlight compensation (BLC) button. Manual iris and manual gain facilities can be found on some cameras. Exposure can also be manipulated to some extent using a shutter speed control or program exposure settings.

Autofocus

A system found on almost all camcorders which automatically adjusts the lens to ensure that the image recorded is sharp. It tends to focus on the nearest object in the centre of the screen.

Autofocus generally works well, although a manual override is essential for focusing on a subject at the side of the frame, or when the autofocus is distracted by foreground objects, lowlight, low-contrast etc.

AWB

Auto white balance is a system in which colours are reproduced in the same way the human eye sees them in a wide variety of lighting conditions.

Although all camcorders have this automatic function, only a few allow you to override it manually in difficult lighting or for creative effects.

Lowlight

All camcorders are capable of recording in very low light. The quoted minimum light level required by today's camcorders ranges from 1–10 lux – but before you pick the one with the lowest rating, you should know that a relatively dimly lit room at night would give you 50 lux. So don't pick a camera on its lux rating.

In truth, although camcorders will give you a picture in the lowest of lights, they give their best results at greater light levels. In dingy lighting colours will be muddy, and the picture will be grainy (thanks to the automatic gain). These kinds of pictures can look atmospheric, but if you can turn up the lighting slightly do.

Fade

A facility on some models which allows you to end a shot by gradually fading away the picture to black (or white) over two or three seconds. You can also fade the scene in.

One of the few creative controls found on most cameras. Gives a professional feel, if used sparingly, say, to mark the end of a day's shooting. Makes a change from the normal hard cut between scenes.

High shutter speeds

Usually camcorders use a shutter speed of 1/60sec (1/50sec on European models). Faster shutter speeds (up to 1/10,000sec) can often be selected manually using a special button or program mode. This allows each frame to be recorded with less blur – especially if the subject is moving.

Of little use. Video recordings are generally played back at normal speed, so if you shoot moving subjects with a fast shutter speed, the image will jump between frames, giving a flickering effect. Only of benefit for analyzing individual frames or to playback in slow-mo – such as in sports training.

Date function

Displays date, time or both when button depressed. Good for keeping a record when each sequence was shot.

Leave it on for just a few seconds at the beginning of each day's shooting –– otherwise will look very irritating on screen.

Program modes

Special shooting modes which change a combination of iris, gain, shutter speed and white balance to suit a particular shooting condition. Commonly found modes include Action, Portrait, Lowlight and High-speed shutter.

Use with care. Portrait mode can increase shutter speed, for example, and lead to jerky pictures. Find out what each program does on your camera, so you know its shortfalls. Poor alternative to true manual overrides, but better than no override at all.

Formats

Perhaps the most perplexing decision you have to make when choosing a camcorder is which tape format to go for. There are currently six different formats in common use – each using its own type of tape, and each having its own advantages and disadvantages.

Everyone has heard of full-size VHS, as this is the format that is by far the most commonly used on domestic VCRs (video recorders). VHS's greatest advantage, therefore, is that tapes can be played directly on a VCR – so you don't need the camcorder to play back. You also get long tape running times. The big disadvantage is that the camcorders are very large by today's standards, and need to be supported on the shoulder.

VHS-C is a compact version of VHS, using the same half-inch width of tape, but in a smaller shell. It retains compatibility with VHS VCRs thanks to an adaptor cassette which, when loaded with a VHS-C tape, can be inserted straight into a normal video recorder. However, all camcorders, no matter which format tape has been used, can also be plugged directly into a television for replay.

The 8mm, or Video 8, format was specially designed for camcorder use. As its name suggests, it uses 8mm-width tape in a shell that is little bigger than an audio cassette. Consequently, the 8mm format has a slight upper hand over VHS-C, in that the camcorders are generally a little smaller. Other advantages over VHS-C include longer tapes, and better quality sound on mono models (although stereo 8mm and VHS-C models are on a par). The disadvantage of 8mm is that it is incompatible with VHS, so you have to use the camcorder itself for playback on your TV.

The final three formats are more recent introductions, all designed to give improved picture quality. They are known as high-band formats – offering horizontal picture resolution of up to 400 lines (as opposed to the 240 lines possible with VHS, VHS-C and 8mm, which are known as low-band formats). A further advantage, is that, because the brightness and colour parts of the picture signal are processed separately, you get cleaner, more accurate, colour rendition.

Each of these three high-band formats uses the same cassette shell as one of the low-band formats. S-VHS is the improved version of VHS, S-VHS-C is the high-band equivalent of VHS-C, and Hi8 is part of the 8mm family. However, compatibility within these families is limited. Previously recorded low-band tapes can be replayed in a high-band camcorder, but the reverse is not true. High-band tapes cannot be replayed in a low-band camcorder or VCR. Hence you use the camcorder to replay your footage.

However, the extra quality offered by these formats, especially if you are intending to copy or edit your tapes onto VHS anyway, greatly outweighs these disadvantages. Copying always means a drop in picture quality, so by starting off with the best quality to begin with the end result is more likely to look acceptable.

VHS-C adaptor: this battery-operated device allows you to play a VHS-C tape in a full-size VHS VCR. Mechanical arms extend the exposed tape width to that needed for the larger head drums in a video recorder.

VHS-C & VHS: Although these two cassettes are very different in size, they use the same half-inch metal oxide tape. Because of this the running time possible with a VHS-C tape is significantly shorter than with 8mm – but is still long enough for most occasions. Full-size VHS camcorders are, nowadays, primarily used in schools and institutions where the tape is likely to replayed when the camcorder is being used by the next department or class.

8mm: the shells of the 8mm (or Video 8) tape format are little bigger than an audio cassette. It uses a special metal-coating in order to pack the required information into the 8mm tape width. It is the most popular tape format in most countries of the world, although it has no real technical advantages over its main, low-band rival – VHS-C.

The White Balance

Of all the functions found on a camcorder, it is undoubtedly the white balance system that newcomers find the most mysterious. When the human eye sees a piece of white card it looks white whether it is lit by candlelight, the moon or the midday sun. In fact, different light sources have their own colour – which should make the white card take on that colour. Human vision automatically compensates for these variations. A camcorder's CCD chip needs to be told, or to work out, what type of light it is working under – hence the white balance system.

The colour of sunlight itself varies enormously from the fiery glow of a tropical sunset to the deep blue of a summer sky. Typically it is slightly blue in colour, whilst indoor bulb light (known as tungsten lighting after the metal often used for its filaments) is predominantly orange.

One of the commonest problem areas are sun-

sets. A camcorder can mistake the orange colour for tungsten lighting, and to try to correct for this and you end up with an insipid shot that lacks the depth of colour of the original. Some camcorders have sophisticated systems, or special program modes, to help you get over this problem. Other camcorders give you the option of manual control.

There are two types of manual white balance control. Sometimes you are given a number of presets to choose from – so that you can tell the camcorder which type of lighting you are using (or want the camcorder to think you are using). Alternatively the manual white balance is set by pointing the camera at a piece of white paper (or a special white lens cap) and pressing the white balance set button. In this case you are, in effect, telling the camcorder that what it is seeing is white and to adjust its electronic colour filtration so that it is recorded as such.

1: With the white balance set for a very high colour temperature, such as found on a beach or ski slope in bright sunshine, this scene takes on a reddish cast.

2: The white balance is properly set and the colour rendition of the shot is correct.

3: With the white balance set for indoor bulb lighting (tungsten) the shot takes on a bluish cast.

Holding the Camera

Steadiness when hand-holding the camera should be one of the first techniques that you should master. Camcorders today weigh little more than a 35mm SLR stills camera. Whilst this greatly reduces the strain of carrying a video camera about (and for those of us who used the technology 15 years ago that's no small achievement) it does make them more difficult to hold steady. What's more, the miniaturization of camcorders has meant there is less to get hold of to keep things steady – very few models survive that can be plonked on the shoulder.

In order to hold the camera steadily in front of the eye, you must first adopt a comfortable stance. Your feet should be about a foot apart, and your elbows tucked into your sides to give firm support to the camera. Make sure that the strap is tight around your right hand to support the main weight. Use your left hand to steady the camera by placing the palm of this hand on the underside of the camera.

If you have to move the camera to follow the action, turn your body from the waist, don't just move your head. Keep these movements whilst recording slow and deliberate, so they don't appear jerky on screen.

Perhaps the best lesson to learn is to minimize these movements as much as possible. Most beginners are too keen to change their position and move the camera round whilst they are recording. In fact what you should be trying to do is to break down your video into a series of shots. Record part of a scene for a few seconds, put the camera into pause, then look for a different angle on the same subject, or for something else to shoot. Only when you have this next subject framed up in the viewfinder should you record again.

You will also soon find that holding the camera steady is much more difficult when using the telephoto end of your zoom lens. For this reason it is always best, when you have the choice, to get closer to your subject and record using the wider settings of the zoom. This not only minimizes camera shake, but also means that the microphone will pick up the sound more easily.

Fortunately, more and more of today's camcorders are building in image stabilization systems, which are designed to keep the picture steady even at the telephoto settings. To begin with, these shake-busting systems had a downside – the picture was steadier but there was also a slight deterioration in image quality. Today the optical

Left: The normal way to hold a camcorder is to take the main weight on the right hand, tightening the wrist strap so the camera doesn't slip. The left hand then simply steadies the camera. Stand with your legs slightly apart, and with your elbows tucked into your body. Occassionally a monopod ofers extra support.

Left: Leaning against a wall is a good way of gaining extra support for shots which last more than a few seconds or when using the telephoto end of the zoom.

Above and left: Brace yourself when angling the camera downwards. Use a convenient support, such as a chair, if you can, or put one knee on the ground and support your arms on the raised knee.

Right and below: At outdoor events you usually have to improvise. For low shots, you may prefer to lie on your front, like a marksman. A sitting position will give a higher angle – use your knees for support.

Above: A car roof provides another stable platform to lean against.

and digital stabilization systems can work without degrading the picture.

Whatever type of camcorder you use, it is worth getting into the habit of looking for extra support when you are shooting. A wall, a doorway, even the back of a chair, can be used to give you something to lean against. For low-angle work, kneel and rest your right elbow on your knee, or lie prone with the camera resting on your gadget bag.

Using a tripod

No matter how proficient you become at hand-holding the camera, you will never achieve the absolute steadiness that comes with using a tripod. For the professional a good tripod is not an option, it is essential. Choose a good-quality, sturdy model. Don't be persuaded that a lightweight model that folds up to a tenth of its extended size is the one to buy. A good tripod should be a bit of a nuisance – its size and weight are its virtues.

When buying one, remember that it will seem more sturdy on the smooth floor of a showroom than it will on rough ground with a 30-mile-an-hour wind howling round its legs. Check how high you can raise the camera platform – it should reach your eye level at the very least. Also see how far the legs will splay for low-angle shots.

The head of a video tripod is different from that on a photographic one. For a start it only allows movement in two directions – there is precious little need for upright shots in video! Second, the video head is designed so that it can be moved whilst you are shooting. The panning action (movement from side to side) and tilt action (movement up and down) should be as smooth as possible. Check these movements in the shop – make sure they are even, and that there is some sense of weight and resistance to the action.

A further difference from the photo tripod, is that video heads have a locating pin just in front of the screw that attaches to the camera. This engages with a second hole on the base of the camera, and ensures that the camera can't rotate when in position. Another useful feature is a quick-release plate. This allows you to take the camera on and off the tripod in a hurry, without having to fiddle around unscrewing the main bolt.

Although the tripod is an important accessory for the serious video maker, it is rather too cumbersome for some applications – when you have to physically carry all your gear, or when you are rushing through crowds from one shot to the next. In these circumstances, there are lots of accessories available to give you a touch more support. One of the most common is the monopod, the one-legged tripod, which allows you to rest the weight of the camera on the ground, and gives you great flexibility for panning – an ideal companion for sports fixtures or street carnivals.

An alternative is the shoulder brace or chest pod. These curious looking attachments allow you to use your own shoulder or ribs as a further support. Other devices include clamps for attaching your camera to farm gates, shelves and tables, and car supports with a sucker which attaches to a window for shooting your own road movie.

Above: A mini tripod can be used for shooting from a table-top or shelf, but is no substitute for a full-sized tripod. This model doubles as a shoulder brace.

Left: A chest pod allows you to brace the camcorder against your body for extra support, but it also allows you to move quickly between shots. Useful when working in crowds, such as at an airshow or carnival.

Below: One of the most important features in a tripod is versatility. For example, you may need a tripod-mounted camcorder for low-angle shots. In this case, a tripod that allows you to splay the legs wide so that the camera is very near the ground will be ideal.

Left: A heavy tripod is not always the most mobile piece of equipment. A dolly is a set of wheels that attach to the feet of a tripod. This not only makes manoeuvring between shots easier, it can also be used to move the camera smoothly whilst recording, for tracking or crab shots.

Right: When choosing a tripod check that the head allows you to perform smooth, steady pan and tilt shots.

Exposure

The lens on a video camera is constructed using the same optical principles as the lens on a stills camera. The amount of light entering the camera is controlled by increasing or reducing the lens iris – an aperture of overlapping leaves creating a hole of a variable diameter. Today, all camcorders have automatic exposure, by which they continually adjust the iris according to the lighting conditions.

Typically an exposure system will take brightness readings from twenty or more different areas across the image. Comparing these readings from an information bank in its memory, the system can work out the type of lighting condition and decide how the scene should look on screen.

As with all automatic functions, there are occasions when even sophisticated systems will have problems. The first can occur when you move quickly from an area of sunlight to shade – a momentary jump in brightness on screen may be noticed on tape. Second, when your subject is brightly lit in an otherwise dark scene, the camera will tend to overexpose – trying to get detail into the shadows, when you'd rather not have any. Most commonly, if the subject is backlit, with bright areas in the background of the image, the main part of the image will be underexposed.

The problem with video is that it just cannot cope with very contrasty scenes – where some parts are brightly lit, and others are dark. The human eye can cope with a contrast ratio of 100:1 – where the highlights are a hundred times brighter than the deepest shadows. Camcorders, can only cope with a contrast ratio of around 30:1. High-contrast scenes – such as found on a sunny beach might have a contrast ratio of up to 500:1. The camcorder has to make a compromise – some parts will be burnt out to pure white, whilst others will fill in to pure black.

Unfortunately, only a few of today's camcorders give you full control over the aperture. You may get a backlight button – which opens up the aperture to ensure that your subjects do not become silhouettes when the sun is behind them.

The only other ways to change the exposure setting if you have auto-only exposure are either to try the different program modes you have to see if they will improve the result, or to recompose the picture slightly to get round the problem. Cropping the picture a little so that your main subject fills the frame more completely, and so there is less of troublesome background in shot, normally does the trick.

2: Many stills cameras would have great difficulty in achieving an image in lighting conditions such as these. Video cameras have a greater light sensitivity and can operate in very dim light. With automatic exposure, the camera will tend to set exposure for the overall lighting, rather than for the bright area at the end of the tunnel.

1: Shooting from deep shadow into bright sunlight can cause problems when using automatic exposure: the camera cannot decide which to use as a standard, and the exposure 'wobbles' between the two extremes. If this happens, set exposure manually or reframe the shot.

3–4: When the subject moves from one lighting environment to another, there will be a noticeable lag in exposure at the point of transition, as the automatic exposure controls seek to determine the new exposure levels. The only way to avoid this is to break the sequence into two different shots.

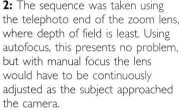

1: For fast action sequences, the autofocus system on most camcorders proves to be invaluable. In a situation like this, however, there is the danger of water spray confusing the focusing system. Do a trial run and check through the electronic viewfinder.

2: The sequence was taken using the telephoto end of the zoom lens, where depth of field is least. Using autofocus, this presents no problem, but with manual focus the lens would have to be continuously adjusted as the subject approached the camera.

Focusing and Depth of Field

If there is one thing that is going to ruin your videos, it is going to be out-of-focus footage. A lot of things will be excused by the people in your audience, but if they can't clearly see the main part of the picture on screen they'll soon complain.

Fortunately, practically every camcorder sold today has an autofocus system that makes sure that your pictures are sharp most of the time. For those other occasions, you can at least see in the electronic viewfinder that the shot is blurred – so you will know it is time to switch to manual focus.

There are two types of autofocus system in common use. Infrared (or active) systems measure subject distance by sending out one or more beams of infrared light. The beam hits the subject and returns to the camera; by calculating the angle at which it returns, the camera can work out the distance. The second system is known as passive autofocus, and this works by analyzing the picture focused on the CCD. It works on the principle that a sharp picture is more contrasty than an out-of-focus one – and therefore moves the lens in search of the highest contrast picture it can find.

Both systems have drawbacks. Infrared systems,

for example, have problems with focusing through glass or with mid-range distances when using long telephoto lens settings. Passive systems, on the other hand, struggle in very low light, or with low-contrast subjects (such as a plain wall).

Manual focusing

Manual focus is therefore essential in some circumstances for technical reasons. But it is also a good creative tool. It ensures that people walking in front of the camera when videoing a speech at a wedding, for instance, do not make the focusing change. You may also want all of the scene out of focus – gradually sharpening the image to start a new sequence. Or you may want to highlight just part of the scene in focus, de-accentuating the rest by making it blurred.

Autofocus generally works well with moving subjects, but if the image is moving very fast across the viewfinder the AF system can have problems keeping up. In these circumstances it is best to focus manually on a predetermined spot that is going to allow you to get as much sharp footage as possible for that particular shot.

3–4: The two shots above, taken from a video made on a school sports day, show the effect of depth of field. Notice how the runners come out of focus as they approach the camera.

5–7: For this sequence at the sports day, the focus was set up manually. It was important that all the runners across the track were in focus, and not just those nearest the camera. This meant a relatively large depth of field was required, so focus was set using the wide angle of the zoom lens. As with other situations, it is a good idea to rehearse the shot before actually taking it.

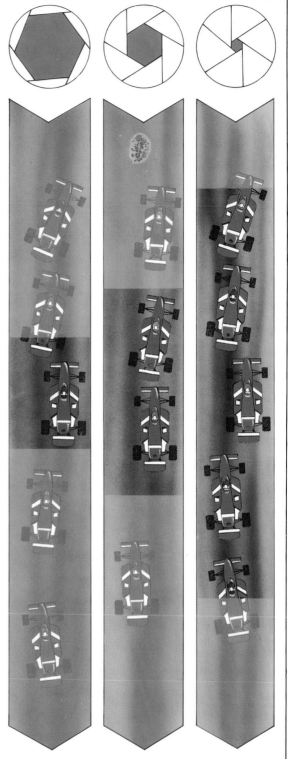

DEPTH OF FIELD

Depth of field is the distance between the nearest and furthest objects that are in focus in any given shot. Depth of field is greater at the wide-angle end of the zoom and least at the telephoto end (it also depends on the size of the lens aperture and on the distance from the camera to the subject). Depth of field extends further behind the subject than it does in front. The limited depth of field at the telephoto end of the lens can be used to isolate subjects, or to put the background out of focus. Conversely, a shot taken at the wide-angle end of the lens, focused on a distant object, will give great depth of field.

35

1: This video about the life of a convent was introduced with a sequence of scene-setting shots of the building itself. This began with a very long shot of the convent, which was followed by progressively closer shots.

2: After the initial shot a different camera position was adopted directly in front of the building. The lens gradually panned down and zoomed in towards the door and the first human element was introduced in the shape of the approaching figure.

The Range of Shots

A shot is a section of continuous, uncut footage and is the basic unit of video work. The three basic shots are the close-up, the mid-shot and the long-shot – CU, MS and LS in the abbreviations used in the television and film industry. They are defined in terms of human subjects, although of course they apply to shots of landscapes and all inanimate objects too.

A close-up is a head-and-shoulders shot of a single person. When only the full face occupies the screen, the shot becomes a big close-up (BCU). Any closer than this (a shot of the eyes or mouth only, for instance) and you have an extreme close-up (ECU). Each gives what the audience perceives as an increasingly intimate view of the subject.

BCUs and ECUs are therefore only used rarely.

The mid-shot extends to just below the waist (notice not *to* the waist – cut-off points that correspond to human sections look odd on television). The mid-shot concentrates on the subject, but includes a sense of background. Where a shot contains two people it is a 'two-shot'.

The long-shot contains the full human figure, from head to toe. It also tells the viewer where the subject is and how he or she relates to the environment. The long shot can extend to become a very long-shot (VLS) and an extreme long-shot (ELS).

Whilst these definitions are mainly for general guidance, helping the writer or the director tell the

3: Details can be very revealing. This was a building with a long history and the camera could record many close-ups that reflected the fact.

4: Each detail shot is recorded for just two or three seconds – and can be composed exactly like stills photographs.

5: Look out for the bizarre or unusual to prompt interest, or humour, amongst your audience.

camera operator the kind of shot required, they also form a useful shorthand with which to plan your video. By writing down the different shots you hope to get you will begin to see how your video is acquiring a sense of pace and rhythm.

Motivated shots

Each basic shot has a different emotional impact upon the viewer, which should be kept in mind when shooting a subject. Notice how on television a newscaster is never shown in more detail than a close-up. The big close-up or extreme close-up implies an intimacy that would be inappropriate (such shots tend to be reserved for an emotional response and are intrusive, bringing us closer to the subject than would happen in real life). Similarly, someone talking in long-shot appears distanced and isolated. It is obvious that they are talking to the camera and not to us.

Of course, shots must not be considered in isolation but be related to the preceding and following images. In most situations these different shots should have a similar feel about them and the transitions should not be too great. A move from extreme long-shot to close-up would be obtrusive, and the progression would be better broken down

working through extreme long-shot, long-shot, mid-shot and close-up. The reverse is also true: if you are about to take a second shot of the same subject from a different angle, the change is much more effectively achieved if you change shot size too. So, if the first shot was in mid-shot, begin the second in long-shot or close-up.

Make a video of an everyday subject – preferably in an outdoor location, such as a street market – and explore the effect of different shots and the way they relate to each other. In the ideal tape, each shot inevitably flows into the next, with the audience being unaware of the camerawork. A common mistake made by many beginners is in timing the duration of the shot: the camera either lingers too long on a scene in which nothing is happening, or it darts from shot to shot in an irritating, fragmented way. The first error can be avoided by common sense – if nothing is happening, why are you recording it? The second is cured by experience. Tell yourself to hold your shots that bit longer than you feel is necessary. Also ask yourself why you are moving from one shot to another. Unless there is a good reason (perhaps to take in the background or to catch an expression on a face) the shot will probably fail on screen.

1: An amusing moment in the life of the sisters was captured using a wide range of different shots. The sequence began with a very long establishing shot giving a broad view of the location and what was going on. Note that a long-shot is not necessarily taken with a wide-angle setting, it can also be taken with the telephoto end of your zoom.

2: Individual characters can be introduced in long-shot – an ideal way in which to show gesture and body movement.

3–4: With a subject involving action you will have to be prepared to move the camera and follow the subject – as well as occasionally zooming in or out slightly to keep your subject in the frame.

5: From close-up to long-shot: as the gardener walks into the distance the shot lengthens before your eyes. This is a type of shot that can be used effectively to end a sequence.

Obtaining Coverage

Before beginning any video project you should work out exactly what you want to achieve. Consider this example of a video showing a tightrope walker in action.

The first point is to show where the performance is happening. And what is that building in the background – is it a barn or a house? Is the performer approaching through empty streets to practice? Or is he passing excited children, queuing early for his performance? Filming, like writing, is a matter of providing signals, pointing your viewers in the right direction. You must also satisfy them with certain basic information. Hopefully, once hooked, they will stay to the end.

You also need to tell the viewers who your characters are. If the performer has been hired for a children's birthday party you need to make clear which child is having the birthday, and perhaps which of the adults are his parents. If a previously unseen character appears three-quarters of the way through the tape, the audience will wonder who it is.

Next, consider the performance itself. Do you want to show the performer getting ready or do

2: The next shot reveals the tightrope walker in action. At this point there is enough interest to keep the same camera position.

3: The tension builds up as the performer reaches halfway – will he make it across the rope?

4: There is a temptation to zoom in as the tightrope walker loses his footing – but this would be a mistake because if we could not see the space around him we would miss the sense of danger.

5: The same position is held as the performer regains his balance. This again shows a good reason for not cropping in too close with the zoom. We don't know when the performer is going to move up or down, or forwards and backwards – and we don't want to miss any of the action by guessing wrongly.

you want him to make a dramatic entrance? With a tightrope act, the excitement lies with the performer balancing on the wire. Close-up shots of his feet will convey the precariousness of his position, but a VLS will also give an indication of the surroundings and how far off the ground he is positioning. At a children's party the range of reactions from delight to fear will be worth including.

By thinking critically about the narrative and asking such questions you will avoid elementary mistakes and convey the full atmosphere of the event. Make a list of scenes and decide how you will treat each one – long-shot, mid-shot or close-up? Having done that, you must then turn to practical considerations, and in particular to the question of whether you intend to edit in-camera.

As far as coverage of the tightrope walker is concerned, the ability to edit after shooting gives you the ability to cut unsuccessful parts.

In this case, a wide-angle shot of a farmyard, showing the performer setting up the wire, would establish the setting and theme of the video. A zoom-in shot (ending as an MS) of one of the spectators' facial expressions would show the sense of drama of the occasion. All of these shots would be taken with a tripod-mounted camera.

The actual performance should also be rehearsed and shot from a tripod, although the camera would need to be repositioned. A good impression of the act calls upon a very long-shot, long-shot, mid-shot, and big close-ups of the performer's face, hands and feet. Since this is a private performance, the tightrope walker could be persuaded to repeat the act a number of times while each separate shot is set up, rehearsed and then recorded.

I–2: The tightrope act involved a number of tricks, each of which had to be rehearsed before the actual shots were recorded. A zoom shot was used for this one-legged balancing stunt.

3: The jump is the most spectacular stunt in the act. From the video point of view the challenge here was to get the framing right – too close, and the performer would leave the frame, too distant, and the jump would seem insignificant.

4: The sequence continues with the tightrope walker repositioning himself after the jump.

5: In the final shot before he jumps down to take a bow, he has regained his balance and his poise once more.

I: A high-angle shot of this game at a children's party gives a sense of the whole scene. Standing on a chair or table gets the camera into a recognizably different shooting position. It could then be complemented by low-angle shots giving the 'child's-eye view' of the situation.

Camera Angles

The 'normal' position for the camera when shooting is at eye level, pointing straight ahead. Such a shot maintains the illusion that everything on screen is seen as the viewer would find it in 'real life'. But shoot from a high or low angle and a completely different effect is conveyed.

Low-angle shots have a number of uses. Most obviously they can be used to convey the point of view of one of the subjects in the video – that of a child, for example, or of someone lying in the grass. In the video of the tightrope walker, the low-angle shot exaggerates the height of the wire above ground and adds to the drama. But in other cases a low-angle shot conveys impressions of submission and authority.

The cliché 'looking up to someone' conveys a truth about the way human beings see one another. That is why executives often make sure that their chair is just a little higher than any other in the office. And it takes only a relatively small deviation from the horizontal to convey this effect of dominance in video, so check that you are not unintentionally doing so. High-angle shots have the opposite effect, placing the viewer in a position of authority, looking down on the subject. Shoot at the eye level of your subjects in normal circumstances – even if this means kneeling when shooting the children.

Both high- and low-angle shots, especially when taken with the wide-angle end of the lens, can create a sense of distortion and threat. Shots with a distorted perspective, pointing up the side of a tall building from directly beneath, for example, can convey the point of view of an unseen intruder.

While these shots undoubtedly add visual variety and excitement to your videos, it is dangerous to overuse them, or to use high- and low-angle shots in an inappropriate context.

Pans, tilts, cranes and crabs

A pan is the sideways movement of a camera from a fixed position. It can be used to reveal more of the surroundings of a given location, or to follow the movements of a character. Like all camera movements, the pan should be executed slowly and deliberately, giving the audience time to assimilate the changing image.

A tilt is a 'pan' executed in the vertical plane, and may be used to reveal detail in locations and buildings – a tilt shot up the side of a building, for example, might be used to imply that someone who has just entered is climbing the stairs.

Both pan and tilt shots can be combined with the zoom. For example, you could have a pan shot of someone walking towards the camera at an angle, and gradually zoom in on the subject. Such a shot should be rehearsed beforehand.

The rule for both pan and tilt shots, whether combined with zoom or not, is to plan for the end of the shoot. The audience expects something to be revealed, but if the expectation is unfulfilled the shot loses its motivation.

In addition to these shots are those taken when the camera moves with the action. These are tracking, crabbing and craning shots. Tracking involves moving alongside a moving subject, with the consequent problem, for the home video-maker at least, of camera shake. Crabbing is a movement around the subject in an arc. It is an effective shot giving a three-dimensional view of the subject and its surroundings. Craning means raising the camera whilst recording.

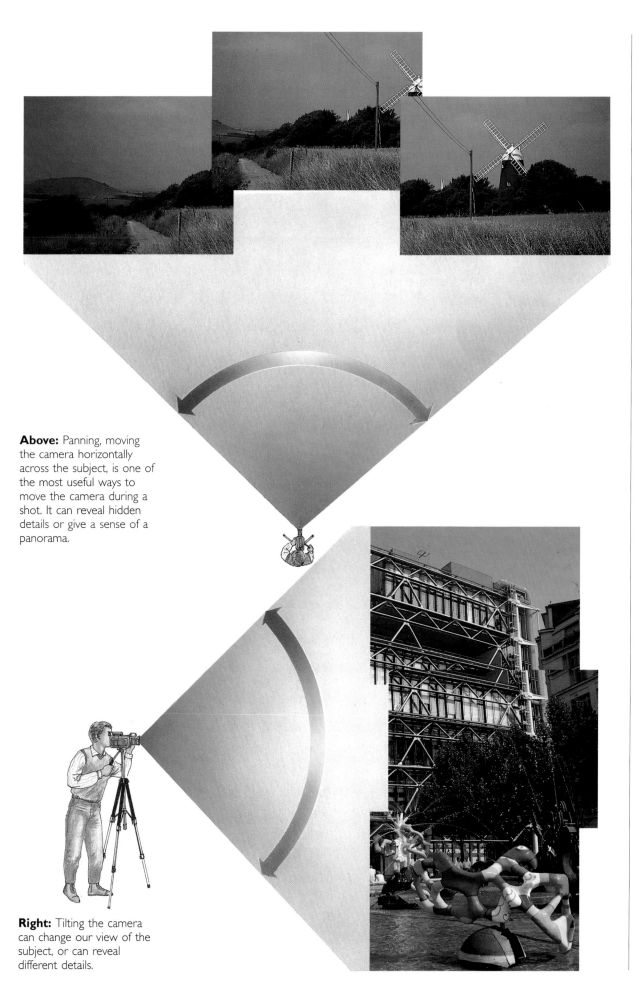

Above: Panning, moving the camera horizontally across the subject, is one of the most useful ways to move the camera during a shot. It can reveal hidden details or give a sense of a panorama.

Right: Tilting the camera can change our view of the subject, or can reveal different details.

Audience Expectations

The television has made us extremely familiar with a huge variety of moving images. Scenes covering everything from famine to sporting triumphs are fed into millions of homes each day. The result is that people have high expectations about the quality of moving pictures, and these expectations are the ones by which your home video will be measured.

At the simplest level, this means your screen subject should not wobble about. It also means that everything you show must be part of the narrative – if you move a shot from a building to a person there must be a good reason for doing so. If you don't have one the viewers will supply their own, which may well result in dreadful confusions. And most importantly, the images you show should reveal a single viewpoint, be readily acces-

sible, and enable the audience to forget that the film is an artificial construct. At least half the art in making good videos involves producing a seamless whole. The audience should be aware of the story and not your techniques. The more sophisticated your videos, the better you should be at hiding your art, no matter how sophisticated it is.

You should also remember that audiences expect events to happen in a particular order and in a certain way. This is especially likely if they are watching coverage of something with which they are familiar – like the wedding featured here. If so, you should aim for the best balance of the predictable and unusual in your coverage. In this way you will satisfy the people who want the obvious shots and sequences, while preventing the boredom of those who want something more.

1: A favourite scene at most weddings is the cutting of the cake. Start with a broad establishing shot of the whole gathering before moving in to record the expected close-up of the bride and groom.

2–3: At the beginning of the shot, we keep to a medium long-shot, to keep the cake and couple in view. As they cut it, the camera then slowly zooms in to record the couple's smiling faces.

4–5: In this sequence of merrymaking at the wedding reception, mid-shots and close-ups alternate with long-shots showing the whole scene. After seeing the girl playing the violin, the audience expects to see the guests listening or dancing. Note also how we switch from a low-angle to high-angle shot to keep things looking interesting.

6–8: The alternate close-ups and long-shots continue, with the general mood of merriment mirrored in the smiling faces of the guests. This type of sequence requires careful planning to allow you to get from one position to another, but it is worth the effort.

Lighting Units

Modern camcorders are able to produce pictures under very poor lighting conditions. Figures as low as one lux are often quoted by manufacturers. In rooms where you wouldn't even be able to read a paper you can record a recognizable picture. Because of this, you would imagine there should be no difficulty videoing in normal domestic interiors, which at around 50 lux are far more brightly lit than this minimum.

Even so, compared with daylight, domestic interiors are very dimly illuminated. For example, the figure on sunny days can be as high as 50,000 lux. So the video camera has to cope with a very wide brightness range. In addition, the video camera has the problem of colour variation between indoor light and daylight to contend with. The human eye is very good at compensating for this great range of conditions, but the video camera operates at its best in a narrower range. For crisp, clear, really watchable videos, most machines prefer a level of at least 1,000 lux.

The problem is not simply that the camera's image sensor is not so sensitive at low light levels. Low light levels often mean diffuse lighting and the modelling of the subject is unlikely to be satisfactory. The lack of contrast that results will mean that different planes in the picture will seem poorly differentiated.

Artificial light

For all these reasons, professional video makers take care to light their subjects with meticulous attention to subject modelling and overall contrast. The amateur must strive to get the best results possible with the time and resources available. To meet this need, a wide variety of lighting units of varying powers and beam-spreads have been developed, many of which have been designed with the hobbyist in mind.

Most video lights are portable and relatively inexpensive, and can be very useful for improving the lighting conditions when shooting indoors

LIGHTING ON A TIGHT BUDGET

If you do not want to go to the expense of buying even more equipment just for the occasional indoor shot of the family, remember that there is a lot you can do to improve the lighting in a room without much hassle.

For a start you can turn on all the lights in the room, and add table lamps and desklights from other rooms as fill-ins where necessary. Don't have all the lights pointed directly at your subjects – have some to light the background, and others bouncing light off walls and ceilings. By careful arrangement of these lights you should at least get a less grainy picture than if managing without.

Another low-cost tip is to use reflectors to bounce light back into shadow areas. Reflectors are sold by video and photographic specialists. However, you will find that a large piece of white card will do just as well – or you could try covering it with silver foil. Place the reflector on the other side of the subject, just out of frame. This will soften shadows and make for a more pleasing result.

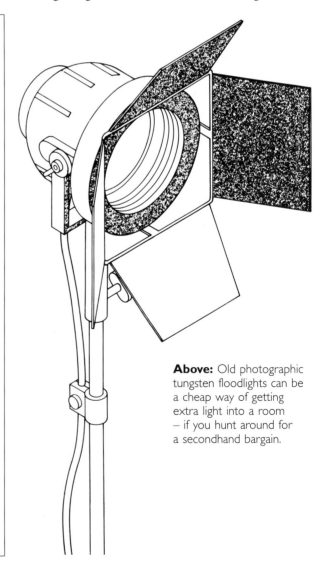

Above: Old photographic tungsten floodlights can be a cheap way of getting extra light into a room – if you hunt around for a secondhand bargain.

at night. Care must be taken when using them, however, because although they increase the quantity of light, they don't always improve the quality.

Many lights with outputs of around 20 or 30 watts are designed to be used on the camera itself – even on the accessory shoe, if your camcorder has one, or on a specially designed bracket (that fits to the tripod bush under the camera, or clips between the camera and the battery). The disadvantage of these lights is that they provide a harsh directional light that can kill the atmosphere, and create hard, ugly-looking shadows on walls directly behind the subject.

More powerful video lights with ratings from 100 to 1,000 watts are designed to be used away from the camera – either held by an assistant, clamped to a shelf, or on a separate stand. They are either mains powered or come with their own rechargeable battery pack.

The power of these lights means that the lighting can be softened (by bouncing the light off a ceiling or by putting a diffuser in front of them) without reducing the brightness so much that you might as well have not bothered! Fan cooling is definitely a feature worth looking out for on these high-output lights as they can get very hot (this not only makes it unpleasant to work under, it also makes the metal casings very dangerous to touch).

Another form of artificial lighting worth considering is old photographic tungsten floodlights. These are still made and are not very expensive – and are very good value secondhand. These plug into the mains and allow you to change bulbs from 150–500 watts to vary brightness.

Left: Some high-powered video lights come with their own shoulder power packs – to give you mobility, as well as a long running time between charges.

Below: Two common types of on-camera video light. The one on the camera at the front fits between the camera's battery and the camera itself. The one behind fits on the accessory shoe and uses its own rechargeable battery.

Above: Many small, modern camcorders do not have accessory shoes for mounting video lights on. A bolt-on accessory shoe such as this attaches to the tripod screw under your camera so that you have somewhere to attach a light (or microphone).

Lighting Set-Ups

The most basic of video lighting set-ups is illumination from a single lamp. Its most common application is to be found in the 'sun-gun', so-called because it is either used to boost poor daylight or employed at night to make filming possible in what are essentially 'newsreel' situations.

Using a sun-gun is basically a one-man professional technique. A battery-operated lamp unit is mounted on top of the camcorder, thus providing a fully portable light which is always aimed straight at the subject. Whilst it has its uses in amateur video, this type of single-lamp frontal lighting is not very pleasing aesthetically – it produces a harsh effect with very little modelling. But it does provide a useful last resort if you are recording material in poor light and do not have the time or the assistance to create a more elaborate set-up.

It is possible to improve the modelling, to give more of an idea of the subject's three-dimensional form, by detaching the lamp and getting an assistant to angle it towards the subject from one side. This can be a good technique for informal shots such as outdoor parties and beach scenes at night, but it is not an acceptable alternative to properly balanced lighting using a number of separate lamps positioned around the subject in a controlled set-up as in a proper studio.

Multi-lamp set-ups

Techniques using multi-lamp set-ups have become established over the years as a means of providing balanced lighting in a studio-type environment. These are professional techniques, but they are easily adapted to amateur use, the 'studio' being replaced by a domestic interior or some other indoor setting where electrical power is available and the conditions for the shoot have been planned ahead and are in your full control.

A typical application of multi-lamp set-ups is the video interview. The scene might be a room in which two people are having a formal discussion. The interviewer is off-camera and the camcorder is being aimed at the main subject, the interviewee, who is sitting in an easy chair. The subject is lit by a main light, known to video makers as a 'key-light', which is aimed from alongside the camcorder. This light alone would produce a strong shadow down one side of the subject's face, so this effect is softened by diffused light coming from a 'fill-light', placed on the other side of the camcorder.

A third lamp can be used to separate the subject from the background. This lamp is usually a spot, and should be aimed from behind the subject's head, to illuminate the hair and give a halo effect. The subject should now be well illuminated, but there may be distracting shadows in the background. A fourth lamp can be brought in to light the background and eliminate any unwanted shadows. Alternatively, if only three lights are available or time is short, the key-light and fill-light can be supplemented by a third light aimed at the background, from which some illumination may reflect back towards the subject's head in any case.

Bounced lighting

One problem with the type of multi-lamp set-up described above is that it works only with a stationary subject – if the subject moves position, the carefully arranged lighting will be rendered useless. Another drawback is that many subjects find the glare from the floodlights unpleasant and difficult to work under. Also, unless the lights are positioned with great care, the results on screen can sometimes appear rather hard and unnatural.

An answer to these problems may be found in

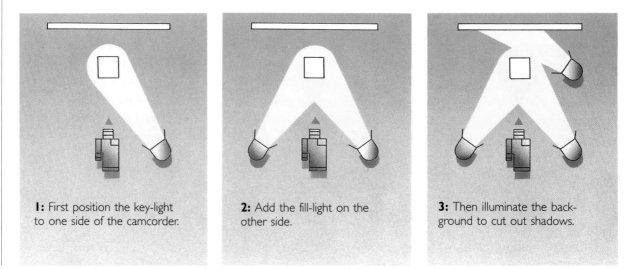

1: First position the key-light to one side of the camcorder.

2: Add the fill-light on the other side.

3: Then illuminate the background to cut out shadows.

Left: Although you can buy specially made reflectors for video and photographic work, you will get results that are just as effective with a piece of white cardboard or hardboard, or a sheet of expanded polystyrene.

bounced lighting. As the name implies, the illumination comes not from a lamp aimed directly at the subject, but from light bounced on to the subject, thus softening the effect and eliminating glare.

Bouncing the light also has the effect of distributing it over a wider area, thereby allowing the subject to move around without affecting the lighting balance too much. In practice, the usual technique is to aim the light upwards and to bounce it either off white ceilings and walls or, if this is not possible, off reflectors made of sheets of expanded polystyrene.

Reflectors

Reflectors can be one of the most useful accessories to have with you when shooting. They provide a cheap and easy way of balancing lighting without the need to bring in extra lamps.

A particularly useful application is found with a subject lit from the daylight coming through a window. The shadow side of the subject will be too dark, and using artificial lighting will be difficult unless you use a lamp that is colour-corrected to match daylight. This is possible by covering the lamp with a special blue filter gel – so the white balance is the same for both light sources.

In order to avoid these problems with mixed lighting, a much easier solution to reflect some daylight back from the window on to the subject's shadow side. Again, a piece of white card, a sheet of expanded polystyrene, or even an unfolded newspaper will do the trick. Outdoors, reflectors are often used to balance strong sunlight by bouncing light into the shadow areas, or to enhance diffused daylight on a cloudy day.

SOME LIGHTING TERMS

Background light Lamp aimed at the background to illuminate it.

Backlight Forward-facing lamp placed behind the subject to illuminate the subject's outline.

Barn doors Adjustable flags attached to the edge of a lamp's housing to allow the direction and spread of the beam to be changed.

Diffuser Material placed in front of a lamp to soften the beam.

Fill-light Lamp introduced to eliminate unwanted shadows from the subject.

Filter Material placed in front of the lamp to change the nature of the light. The most common are coloured filters, which can be used to correct the colour balance of the lighting or provide special effects.

Flood Lamp providing broad, overall illumination.

Key-light The main light in a multi-lamp set-up.

Snoot Conical attachment placed in front of a lamp to narrow the beam width.

Spot Lamp providing a narrow beam of light.

Basic Sound

Sound is too often treated as an afterthought, a secondary consideration to getting the images right. But a poor soundtrack will irritate an audience and can easily spoil what is otherwise a successful video. Conversely, a soundtrack of good quality which has been recorded and compiled with a little thought can often help to mask any visual mistakes.

Remember that sound is being recorded continuously while you are recording images and that the sound is recorded directly on to the tape alongside or beneath the video images. This means that, although it is possible to edit the sound element of your video recordings, it is far easier to get the sound right at the start, while you are actually recording.

The built-in microphone on your camcorder has to be used carefully in order to achieve this. It will probably pick up not only the ambient sound, but also the camera's mechanical noises, the whir of the zoom motor – and perhaps even the grunts and sighs of the operator as well! Although modern camcorders are better than older models in this respect, all on-board microphones suffer from some of these problems.

Another drawback can be the position of the microphone on the camcorder itself. Some models have the microphone located where it can easily be touched with your left hand whilst you are recording. This can have the effect of blocking off some of the ambient sound, while the finger's movement can itself cause unwanted noise on the sound track.

Some, but not all, camcorders have a headphone socket so that you can monitor the sound entering the camcorder's microphone and you should use this for all but the most casual video work. You can use a simple earpiece, such as those used with portable cassette and CD players. Better still, use a pair of enclosed headphones – and ask a friend to monitor the recorded sound for you if you can.

The problems of working with an on-board microphone can be avoided by plugging in an exterior microphone on a long lead. But this is only possible if your camcorder has a separate mic socket – a feature well worth having if you have the choice.

A remote microphone has the added advantage of allowing you to get the microphone close in to the source of the sound. But it will mean that you will have to plan your shooting carefully. Although you want the microphone near to the subject, you will almost certainly want it outside the frame, and this can be a problem. Again, you may have to enlist the help of a friend who can hold the microphone above (or below) the subject and out of shot.

The quality of the sound that you record depends very much upon the environment. Before you begin recording do check that any electrical appliances are turned off. Hard, flat surfaces tend to reflect sound too strongly, resulting in reverberation – an unwelcome echoey quality to the sound. Muffling walls and floors with rugs and blankets can overcome this problem.

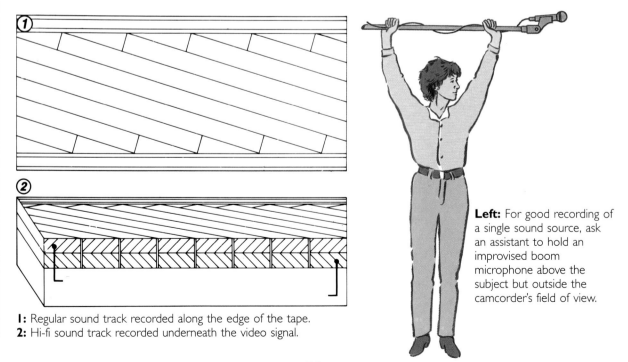

1: Regular sound track recorded along the edge of the tape.
2: Hi-fi sound track recorded underneath the video signal.

Left: For good recording of a single sound source, ask an assistant to hold an improvised boom microphone above the subject but outside the camcorder's field of view.

Alternatively, sound reflectors can be used to direct sound to the microphone. Sheets of hardboard (smooth side facing the microphone) can lift sound when it is too muffled or low.

A particular drawback with low sound, when recording with the on-camera microphone, is that most models automatically boost the signal, so that unwanted noise and recorder rumble increase. A home-made boom microphone constructed with a broom handle often enables you to get closer to the second source, and it is also worthwhile placing a cardboard cone around the microphone to cut out unwanted sounds.

On-camera and extension microphones can be either omnidirectional or unidirectional. An omnidirectional microphone picks up sounds from all around. As such, it is valuable for recording the overall sound of the scene you are filming.

A unidirectional microphone picks up sound in an arc of about 180 degrees. Its advantage is that sounds behind the camera (and the sound of the camera itself) are effectively screened off. A unidirectional microphone is particularly useful for recording informal group shots – friends at a dinner party for example.

Even more directional is the rifle microphone which is superdirectional. Its pick-up cone will not allow you to pick up a single voice from across a crowded street. But as they accept sound from only a 90-degree arc you can match your pictures much more closely to the sound. As such, it is probably the most useful auxiliary microphone you can buy.

With the increasing popularity of television sets that provide stereo sound, along with hi-fi video recorders, video sound tracks in stereo are becoming increasingly popular. There are a number of cameras that can record in stereo. However as the built-in microphones are mounted together on the camera the stereo effect is not very pronounced. An accessory stereo mic has much the same problem. What you really need are two separate mono microphones which are then connected to the stereo mic input through a special adaptor (available from electronic component catalogues or stores). The two mics should then be placed apart, so they each hear slightly different sounds.

The stereo effect will also be destroyed when you pan the camera. So it is far better to mount the mics on separate stands which remain in the same place when you are moving the camera. Exactly where you place the stands will depend on the subject you are recording. An additional advantage of using microphone stands is that they help isolate the microphone from vibrations. If you placed a microphone directly on a table during a dinner party, for example, you would hear a great deal of distorted noise from the plates and cutlery – and very little of the conversation!

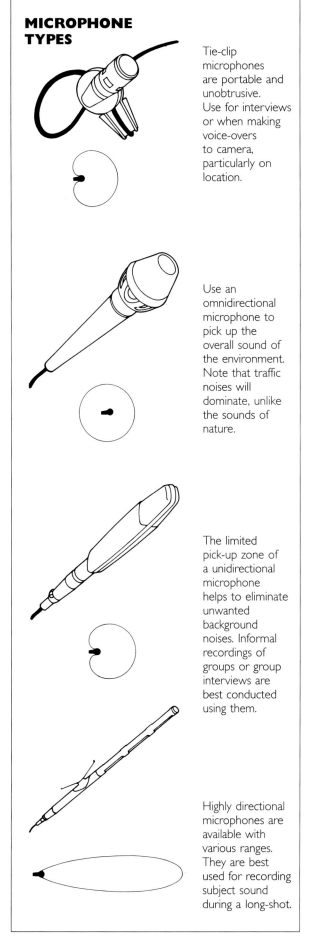

MICROPHONE TYPES

Tie-clip microphones are portable and unobtrusive. Use for interviews or when making voice-overs to camera, particularly on location.

Use an omnidirectional microphone to pick up the overall sound of the environment. Note that traffic noises will dominate, unlike the sounds of nature.

The limited pick-up zone of a unidirectional microphone helps to eliminate unwanted background noises. Informal recordings of groups or group interviews are best conducted using them.

Highly directional microphones are available with various ranges. They are best used for recording subject sound during a long-shot.

Basic Video Editing

The editing of video usually involves the rearrangement of the original shot order and sometimes the opportunity is taken to add to or otherwise to improve the recorded sound. The rearrangement of the shot order has to be done, not by physically cutting the video tape, but by a process of copying it on to a second tape, during which unsatisfactory shots can be dropped and the beginnings and endings of sequences can be tidied up. In the case of sound, the original synchronized sound can be totally replaced or combined with non-sync background effects, music or commentary. The original sync sound can be combined with the additional material though this requires the use of special equipment.

Assemble editing

In essence, 'assemble editing' is quite simple. Basically, all you do is connect two video machines back-to-back so that the original recording – both audio and video – can be played back from the replay or source machine into a record or edit machine. This is known as a 'two-machine edit' and is the basic set-up irrespective of whether the machines are simply controlled manually – as I shall describe – or whether more sophisticated automatic means of control are used. Nothing special in the way of video machines is required, provided that the edit deck has 'backspace edit' – this will be explained in more detail later. It also helps if the machine has 'flying erase' since it will produce clearer edits than with a machine without this facility.

The video interconnection is made by using 'copying leads' which are so called because they have the correct terminations to suit the AV out and the AV in sockets on the respective machines.

In order to help you see what you are doing, you will also need to connect in a monitor screen. An ordinary portable colour TV is quite adequate and its aerial socket should be connected to the 'RF out' socket on the edit machine. We only need one monitor as the 'source' machine pictures are fed to the screen via the 'edit' machine and will show whenever the edit deck is on 'record' or 'stop'. Otherwise, the screen will show the copy tape pictures whenever it is on 'play'.

So far, so good. With your original recording loaded into the source machine (normally your camcorder) and a fresh tape in the edit machine, you can make a start on your assemble edit. To begin, first run the original tape on the source machine to find the start of the first shot to be copied or 'assembled'. Hold the machine on play-pause, and then set the edit machine to record-pause. Then release both machines from pause to play and record respectively. Stop both machines when you have run a few seconds beyond the end of the first section.

The next thing to do is to check that all is well with the copy, so rewind it and play it back, stopping on record-pause when you reach the edit point for the beginning of the next shot. Now you can run the source deck to the beginning of the next section, stopping as before on play-pause. Assemble it onto the copy as before, and continue to the end of the movie.

Although the basis of video editing is this simple, it has to be recognized that it must be done precisely under basic manual conditions for it to work well. If you are not good at pushing buttons simultaneously, you will be better off if your machines have synchro edit sockets. If they have, and you have the special lead to connect them together, you have a convenient way of releasing both machines off pause simply by pressing one button.

Locating edit points

There are also one or two other points to bear in mind. The first is that you should try to minimize the amount of time that the machines are held on pause – otherwise the tapes may begin to wear. So organize the location of the edit points on the source tape in advance. Go through the tape and note the counter readings relative to the beginning of each section so they can be located easily and quickly. Use cue-review and fast replay to speed up this operation. If the search is likely to take time, switch the edit deck to stop. When you are ready to resume the transfer, locate the edit point on the copy tape by repeating the routine already described so that the edit will be made cleanly and exactly at the correct point on the tape.

Another consideration is that you may need to make allowance for the technical feature known as 'backspace edit' on the re-record deck. If you watch carefully, you will find that the first second or so is missing at the start of each new section on the copy. This is because the edit machine, each time it is released from record-pause, takes a little time to start actually recording since it first has to back-track to find and lock on to the video controls signals at the end of the previous section to enable it to make a clean edit without annoying picture break-ups. This can also happen when inserts are being recorded.

Quite often this loss of the beginnings of shots will not matter too much – in fact it may even be a positive advantage in helping you to trim off unwanted material. If, on the other hand, impor-

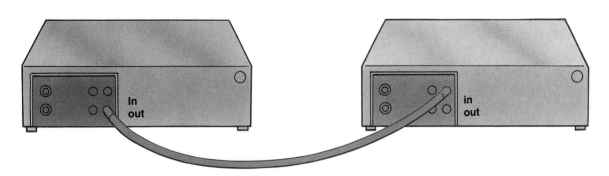

The basis of all editing involves copying from one tape to another. This is done by simply connecting one video recorder (or camcorder) to another video recorder using a cable.

tant action is being left out, it is necessary to off-set the backspace time, either by setting the tape on the source machine one to one and a half seconds early relative to the true edit point, or to release it from pause later by the same amount of time relative to the edit machine. It may sound complicated but it becomes easier with practice!

If the required dexterity and precise timing of this manual method puts you off you'll be pleased to hear that there are devices available that help to automate the procedure. These edit controllers take command of the transport mechanisms of both machines, so that you can control both from the one console. The camcorder or source deck must usually be controlled by an edit terminal – so it is essential that you have a model with this feature. This link also sends the counter readings from the camera to the controller. By pressing appropriate buttons at the beginnings and ends of scenes that you want to record (called 'in' and 'out' points) the controller can remember which bits you want to record. Once you have chosen all the pieces you want to keep, the controller then assemble-edits them together automatically.

Edit controllers

There is a further editing technique called 'insert editing' which is possible on some camcorders and video recorders of the VHS family. With this, it is possible to replace the original video pictures with completely new material; this is done without erasure of the accompanying mono soundtrack which therefore continues to be heard over the insert.

One application of insert is the edit-ing in of titles onto an existing video. Suppose you have recorded some children taking part in a school sports day. Provided that your recording includes relatively unimportant material here and there which can be sacrificed to make room for

inserts – say, overlong shots of competitors wait-ing at the starting line – titles can be substituted to advantage as 'sub-headings' to major sequences. This will help to reduce dead spots in your movie and give it a more professional look.

The titles – for example, 'Johnnie's Big Race' – are lined up in front of the camcorder. The recorded video is then played back over the cam-corder until the place is reached at which the insert is to begin. Hold it on pause at this point and switch the camcorder (or the video recorder you are copying to) to 'insert', then go to 'stop'. You have now edited the title into the original recording.

In a similar way, the original sound recording can be replaced wholly or in part by inserting new material via the audio-dub facility (again only found on some camcorders and VCRs).

You must appreciate that care has to be taken if you are carrying out insert edits and audio dubs onto the original video tape – a mistake here could spoil the whole recording. It is safer to carry out these operations on a copy in a VCR with these facilities.

An edit controller's job is to take the manual drudgery out of editing.

Sound Editing

As we have already suggested in the section on Basic Video Editing, the original sound recording can be replaced wholly or in part by new material which is recorded on to the video tape via the feature known as audio dub.

By no means all camcorders and video machines have this facility; for instance, 8mm machines with hi-fi FM audio do not enable audio to be redubbed separately from the picture, as the two signals are inextricably intertwined on the tape. It is, however, a feature which is often provided on VHS and VHS-C machines for they have lower-quality sound which is recorded as a low-speed edge track and this can be recorded independently of the video. Even with hi-fi stereo VHS family machines there is a separate redubbable mono linear soundtrack, as well as the hi-fi tracks (which cannot be audio dubbed). Whatever format of camcorder you use, you can still do audio dubs on your edited tape in a suitable video recorder.

Audio dub

Audio dub is a useful creative feature, and it can often be the means of saving a recording which is otherwise spoilt by poor sound – say by wind noise on the microphone. Of course, any new sound which is dubbed in is not, unlike the original audio, perfectly synchronized with the pictures. It therefore has to be limited to general background effects to hide the fact that it is a later addition. Backgrounds suitable for dubbing in are sounds typical of the 'sea-shore', 'countryside' (bird song etc), 'crowds' and so on.

You can either record your own background effects or buy one of the special-effects CDs, records or tapes which are available for amateur use. There are 'mood music' tapes and discs, too.

To dub new audio, you will need to connect a CD player (or whatever) to the audio-in socket on your camcorder or VCR. On some camcorders, though, you have to connect it instead to the microphone socket via a special attenuating adaptor-lead (or use a special microphone mixer).

You should also have some means of controlling the level of the new audio so that it matches that of the original recording on either side of the dub. The simplest way to do this is to feed the signal or signals via an audio mixer. You can use just one channel of this as a volume controller or take the opportunity to mix sound from two or more sources, using the video pictures themselves as cues.

The audio-dub operation (which is 'all or nothing': you erase the original sound on this sound track) is quite straightforward. Having first done a dummy run to establish the sound levels via the TV, set the video machine on play-pause at the dub start-point. Press for audio-dub, start the background source player and release the video machine from pause. Go to stop when you reach the end of the section to be audio-dubbed, so that the original sound can continue from that point.

Commentary and music

So far as assemble editing is concerned, the basic set-up for audio is much the same as for simple audio dub, except that the source is the replay video machine. Bear in mind, though, that there will be a break in the audio recording at each edit restart and the type of background used has to be chosen with this in mind. For this reason, mixing in music is not a good idea unless the lengths of the sections between breaks are long enough to make this practical.

You may also wish to add commentary to your video by superimposing it over the original sync sound. As is the case with background music, this can be recorded whilst the video copy is being assembled, provided that the sections are long enough between breaks for recording lengths of commentary. Otherwise you will have to settle for a full-length audio-dub run after the video has been assembled. In this case, you have to have background sound in place of the original sync sound unless you have a separate hi-fi stereo sound track, which will remain unaltered by the audio dub – so both music and sync sound can be mixed together on playback.

For recording commentary the mixer set-up is used. A microphone is connected to one mixer channel and the background source and/or the replay video machine is connected to one or more of the other channels. The commentary is spoken while watching the source for cues – turn down the monitor speaker while this is being done to prevent 'howl round'. You will

Above: A simple four channel sound mixer.

probably need an assistant to operate the equipment and adjust the mixer levels for you, with the monitoring being done via headphones. Incidentally, it is becoming possible to carry out simple premixing while the original sound is being recorded on the camcorder by using a 'mixer-mic' which has inputs for connection to additional sound sources.

Still more ambitious sound tracks can be built up if you have the facility to 'lift off' the sync sound from the assembled copy video and to transfer it onto a separate sound tape on a recorder with multi-track, sound-on-sound mixing. If the runs are short, say five minutes or so, an ordinary cassette or reel-to-reel machine will be adequate for building up a composite track and laying it back onto the video tape whilst still maintaining approximate sync. For longer continuous runs, speed drift becomes a problem which can only be overcome by the use of a special tape recorder which can be sync-locked to the video signals. These are fairly expensive to buy.

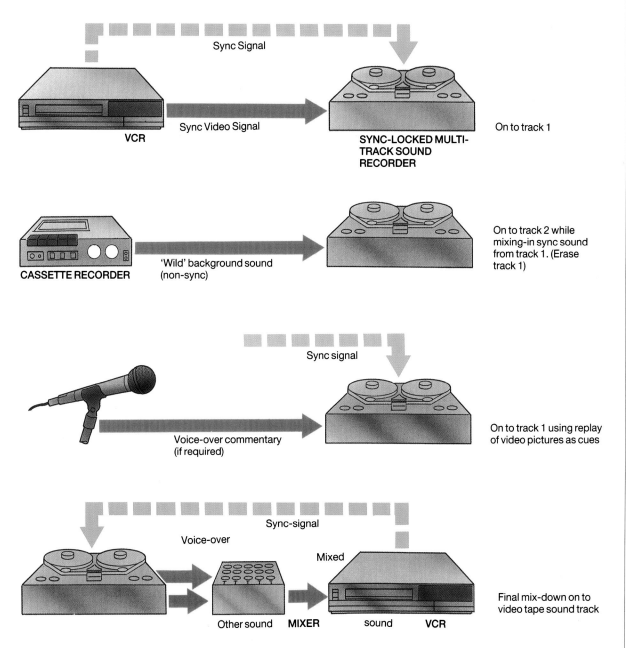

Sync Signal

Sync Video Signal

VCR

On to track 1

SYNC-LOCKED MULTI-TRACK SOUND RECORDER

CASSETTE RECORDER

'Wild' background sound (non-sync)

On to track 2 while mixing-in sync sound from track 1. (Erase track 1)

Sync signal

Voice-over commentary (if required)

On to track 1 using replay of video pictures as cues

Sync-signal

Voice-over

Mixed

Other sound   **MIXER**   sound   **VCR**

Final mix-down on to video tape sound track

1: The first stage in building up the composite video sound track is to record the sync sound effects on your video tape on to track 1 of a multi-track sound recorder.

2: Background sound recorded on location using a portable cassette recorder can next be recorded on to track 2, whilst mixing in the sync effects from track 1.

3: You can now use track 1 of the tape to record a voice-over commentary to accompany your video. This can be recorded in the studio using a microphone if this is required.

4: Finally use a mixer to combine the two sound tracks and record them back on to the video tape in the VCR. Synchronized sound and video are complete on the same tape.

Additional Equipment

The growing mass market in camcorders has brought into being a whole industry devoted to the production of video accessories, which range widely in cost and usefulness. The small advertisements in the video press provide a rich source of information about this type of equipment; a few of the more useful items are described here.

There are many types of lens filters and converters. Screw-on converters can add extra wide-angle or telephoto range to your camcorder's zoom lens. A wide-angle converter is especially useful when shooting in confined spaces, such as small rooms, or when videoing large buildings or wide panoramas. A telephoto adaptor comes into its own for videoing wildlife (although it should be used with a tripod). Filters come in a multitude of different designs – there are polarizing, neutral density, split-screen and multilens attachments, as well as numerous different coloured filters to choose from. Particularly useful are the graduated colour filters – helping to making skies look more interesting, and reducing the overall contrast in the scene (simple colours such as blue and grey work best).

Telecine converters allow you to transfer your old home movies and slides onto video tape. These range from simple screw-on converters to freestanding telecine screens, on to which you can project films for transfer onto tape.

Battery power

Camcorder battery power is a constant preoccupation if you shoot much video away from home, and a spare battery is almost essential. If you need still more power, there are battery belts and shoulder packs that allow you several hours of shooting between charges. Car-operated chargers and special leads that allow you to connect a camcorder to the car battery via the cigar lighter socket are also available. Battery dischargers are another sound investment – helping to ensure that you prolong the useful life and efficacy of your nicads.

Sound recording, dubbing and editing also create a need for extra items. A good set of headphones with large earpieces is vital for good location sound monitoring. A spare single earpiece can also come in useful, as these small items can easily be lost.

There are many different tape recorders and mixers that you can use for sound editing – how far you go depends on your interest and budget. A simple three-channel sound mixer is all it takes to have a basic system. But professional multi-track audio machines with track-to-track mixing and sophisticated cueing arrangements are available for the ambitious video maker.

Wireless microphones are now practical for amateur use. There are reasonably priced units available that consist of lapel microphone, transmitter, and a receiver that you can plug into the camcorder's external microphone socket. With this equipment, you can shoot really professional sound outdoors at a distance from the subject, without running long cables or using bulky stick microphones. Sound can also be captured from a distance by using a gun microphone, but you may need an assistant to operate it. Boom microphones (either purpose-built or improvized with a broom handle) are also useful for gathering exactly the sound you want.

Enhancing the picture

Video-enhancer units are useful when editing. You connect the enhancer between two VCRs when carrying out a 'back-to-back' edit. You can then use the unit to mix the audio and also to improve and modify the picture as it is being copied. Circuits control colour saturation, picture definition and brightness level. Some models also provide direct picture comparison on a single monitor screen. Other types allow you to create 'wipes' and various different masking patterns.

Whilst some camcorders have their own in-built character generators for superimposing titles and other information on the picture, you can buy titling units for use at the editing stage. These vary enormously in the number of typefaces, colours and effect that they offer.

Special-effects generators (see the picture above, for instance) produce a wide range of other changes to the video image. These enhancements start with simple dissolves and wipes that allow you to replace one picture with another, but also include advanced facilities, such as the ability to insert one picture into another. Such techniques, once reserved for the professional edit suite, are becoming increasingly accessible to the amateur.

Tricks of the Trade

They say that the camera never lies. How little do they know – the skilled movie maker can change reality with just a few simple tricks. He or she can turn day into night, a grey sky into tropical sunset, and can turn a suburban living room into an office in the Kremlin. The film industry, of course, has turned the art of special effects into its own multi-million dollar industry, but some of the most effective techniques for distorting the truth don't cost a dime.

Trick shots are not always about duping an audience. Instead they allow you to make a shot or sequence look more dramatic than they were in reality. As with any good storyteller, the audience will allow you to stretch the truth in this way – it's expected of you. In fact, these techniques are so widely used on television, if you don't exaggerate slightly when telling your story you may well end up with a boring video.

Colour Effects

One of the simplest ways to change the look of your shots is by using filters. These are made of glass or optical plastic and screw onto a thread on the front of the camcorder's lens.

Perhaps the most useful type of filter to have in your gadget bag is the graduate. A graduated filter is ideal for those numerous occasions when you are videoing a landscape shot, but the sky is much brighter than the foreground. This can lead to a compromise on exposure, so that either the sky is exposed properly and the foreground becomes a shadowy silhouette, or the sky becomes washed out.

The graduate filter colours, and therefore darkens, the top part of the picture, while leaving the bottom half as it was originally. These filters are available in a wide range of colours, blue is popular as it boosts the colour of the sky, as is grey – as this only darkens the sky without changing its colour.

Also useful for strengthening the colour of a blue sky is the polarizing filter. It cuts down the amount of light from certain parts of the image by only letting in light that is vibrating in one particular plane. By turning the filter on the camera, you can choose which plane by selecting the effect that looks best.

Polarizing filters really come into their own when shooting through glass or around water. By turning the polarizer, you can eliminate all unwanted reflections on the surface of the glass or the water. This is a great help if shooting a shop window display, for instance, or if you want to show the clear depths of a mountain stream.

A neutral density filter is another good buy for the videographer. This darkens the whole picture, and can therefore be used on fully automatic camcorders to open up the aperture on bright days, so you can limit the amount of depth of field in the shot.

If you look through the colourful catalogues produced by many of the filter manufacturers, you'll find that there are hundreds of different filters available, many of which can be used for video. All can be used to good effect, but remember that any filter can be overused.

1–2: Polarizing filters are good at eliminating unwanted reflections from a scene. In picture **1** there is a bright reflection of the setting sun on the opened door. By using a polarizer in shot **2**, this has been completely eliminated.

3–4: Graduated filters not only allow you to add colour to a drab-looking sky, they also allow you to reduce the contrast between sky and foreground. Shot **3** shows the effect with the filter in place, whilst **4** shows the scene unfiltered.

5: A cross-screen filter turns points of light or highlights into stars.

6: Two graduated filters used together can give a very different look to a subject than we might expect to see.

Day for Night

The trouble with trying to shoot video at night is not just that there is not enough light, but also that the contrast between dark and light is too great. The movie industry discovered early on that the best way to shoot a night scene was to film in daylight!

One of the main tricks involved is to change the colour balance of the shots. By using a tungsten white-balance setting in daylight you get blue-tinted pictures, which audiences have come to associate with moonlight.

Changing the white-balance setting alone, however, only gives a subtle result, and is useful only when faking an early morning, dawn scene. For the full 'mock moonlight' effect you have to go a lot further to get a convincing result. For a start you need a darker blue colour to show it is the dead of night – this is done simply by shooting with a dark blue filter (or a couple of light blue colour correction filters).

Next you need to replicate the high contrast ratio found in night scenes. This can be done by shooting directly towards the sun, which provides the contrast between light and shade that you need. But if you leave it like this, you will still see too much detail to make the scene look convincing. The final touch is to underexpose the scene slightly. This not only strengthens the blue filtration, it also increases the amount of shadow area in the picture.

With care, you can even include the moon in the shot. Just wait for the sun to be low enough in the sky and incorporate it into the shot. The result is surprisingly convincing, especially if you use the effect for an establishing shot for an interior sequence, and don't dwell on the technique too long.

As discussed in the last chapter, the other occasion where you can use white balance settings to your creative gain is with sunsets. These can appear washed out when shot with some camcorders, as the auto white balance system can filter out the effect. The answer is to set the white balance system to daylight. However, you can use the same type of filtration externally to make other shots look like sunsets. An orange/red filter is all you need. Remember that the shot must be strongly backlit to look convincing.

1–2: By using a dark blue filter this late-afternoon scene (as shown in picture **2**) has been transformed into what looks like a moonlit view of this Alpine village. Waiting for the streetlights to be switched on was essential for the success of this shot.

3–4: Faking a sunset is easy. All you need is an orange filter and a backlit scene, preferably with the sun in partial view. This before-and-after sequence shows what a difference this simple trick can make.

5–6: This courtyard scene has been made to look as if it was shot at dawn by using a tungsten white balance setting. This has given a light blue tint to the image.

1–2: By cutting from a shot of the outside of this French chateau straight to this grand interior, an audience will assume that the woman is inside the chateau. There's no need, however, for the chateau and the room even to be in the same country. You can use this trick therefore seemingly to show locations that you could never get permission to film.

False Implication

Whenever an audience watches a video it is trying to find connections between shots. It's a natural instinct to try to work out what is going on. Because of this we make assumptions about the language of movies. We know that if we see a shot of the main character looking at something, then the next shot is likely to show what he or she is looking at. If we see a wide shot we assume that this is an establishing shot, showing us the loca-

tion for the next shot, which might be an interior.

A video maker, therefore, not only follows these conventions, but also bends them to suit the purpose of the video. If you want to create some relationship between two different shots, then all you have to do is put them together on screen.

For example, if you wanted to shoot a spy drama with a scene in the Kremlin you may be able to shoot the outside of the building, but you

3–4: By cutting from the above shot of a difficult black run to a shot of a friend skiing straight down a gentler piste, you can create the impression that the two slopes are the same. You may need to angle the camera into the slope to exaggerate the incline on the second shot.

would not get permission to go inside. However, the interior shots could be shot anywhere. So you could cut from the exterior shot straight to your interior and con your audience that it is inside the Kremlin. Of course, it is this same trick that would be used in a Hollywood film on the same subject. In a holiday video, you could use this trick to make it appear that you were staying at the most expensive hotel in town, rather than in a low-grade motel.

Another example of this technique would be to use a shot of a sunset taken thousands of miles away on a different holiday completely, to end the video of this year's vacation.

But it is not just places that can be changed between shots. Actions can be artificially joined together in this way, too. For example you could cut from a shot of someone getting on waterskis for the very first time, to a shot of another water skier jumping over a ramp. If the suits and builds were the same, and you then cut back to a shot of the novice, an audience would assume that the second shot was of the novice too. On these kinds of assumptions, all professional stunts are made. And these tricks can be used in any video. Remember that you will need to add suitable reaction shots from bystanders, and of the subjects themselves, if you are to carry off the illusion.

Repeating the Action

One of the main skills of the video cameraperson is to condense events that take place over hours, or even days, into just a few minutes. The key to success is to keep individual shots short.

But there are times when certain actions cannot be covered with a single shot. You might, for instance, want to show someone going through a door. An ideal sequence would be a shot of our subject approaching the door, followed by a close-up of the key going into the lock, and rounded off with a shot from inside as the door opens and the person goes in. Unfortunately, this is impossible to record as it happens – as you'd have to push past the person as they went through the door. The only answer is to repeat the action, with the subject's cooperation. Each shot is taken separately.

An alternative to this approach is to record each shot, each time the action happens. This might be impractical in the example of the door, but it would work well for a sequence of someone learning to ski, as in the shots here. You can then mix together shots taken from in front and behind without having to overtake your subject. Each shot is taken on different runs down the slope, but sandwiched together it looks as though you were able to record the goings on with several cameras.

1–4: To video a young boy's first attempts at skiing you can record a series of shots taken from different angles on different runs down the nursery slope. You can cut these together as if they were a single run, as the clothes and backdrop remain constant. This adds variety to your coverage and keeps the video short.

5: A shot from behind can be joined with a similar shot taken from the front, such as shot **7**, even if in reality this particular shot ended in a fall (as in shot **6** below).

6: Shots of the boy falling can be re-recorded over (or edited out later) if you want this sequence to show a successful run down the slope.

7: An extreme long-shot from the bottom of the slope shows the progress that the little boy is making. This can be cut to the mid-shot of the boy smiling below.

8: This shot of the boy smiling could have been taken even before he got on the skis, but it makes a great finishing shot to the sequence of his successful run down the mountain.

Set-up Shots

To get some types of action shots you must carefully plan them from the outset. When the action is moving fast, it is almost impossible to get the right framing, exposure, and camera position, just by guesswork alone.

Suppose, as in this sequence, you wanted to record a snowboarder making a jump over a man-made mound. It is easy enough to know where the most spectacular shot is going to be taken from. However, without practising the shot with your subject you are going to risk misjudging how high the snowboarder is going to jump, and how long they are going to stay in the air. The answer is to do a trial run to check out your assumptions. With this type of shot it is quite easy to repeat the action as many times as is necessary, to ensure you have enough coverage. Snowboarders are rarely shy, retiring characters – and will doubtless be pleased to show off their skill.

One of the main problems with this shot is going to be exposure. Not only is the subject going to be framed against a bright sky, but you have the even brighter backdrop of snow to worry about. The camcorder's automatic exposure system is therefore likely to underexpose the shot, turning the snow grey and the snowboarder's face will be silhouetted. With the trial run you can check that the backlight compensation control is going to do enough to correct these problems.

Once the trial run is recorded, you can play it back through the viewfinder to see if the exposure is correct. You can also check that the framing is okay. Have you picked a camera angle that is low enough, and close enough to show how high the snowboarder has jumped? There would be nothing more frustrating than to take this sequence, only to find out when you got home that the jump looked tame, and the slope looked flat.

You can also use the trial run to check the focus. For this type of shot, it is best to focus manually, pre-focusing on a spot just below the mound. If you leave the autofocus in control, you could end up with the lens trying to focus on the sky in parts of the sequence, as the snowboarder leaves the centre of the frame.

Once you have all the controls set up correctly you can then do several takes of the same jump. When editing you can then pick the best sections from each jump and edit them all together, as if they were shot at the same time.

1–4: This sequence of a snowboarder jumping a mound was recorded several times. The best bits were then edited together later, with a suitably dynamic piece of music dubbed over the top, helping to keep the viewers' attention away from the visual joins.

Filling the Foreground

One of the problems with video is that the dimensions of the image cannot be changed. With photography, you not only have the chance of taking upright, portrait, shots as well as horizontal, landscape, ones, you can also crop your prints to whatever size you require. With video you are limited to landscape-shaped images that are four units wide by three units high (known as an aspect ratio of 4:3).

This means that, with certain subjects, it is often difficult to fill the frame with your subject. Landscapes, for instance, are usually much wider in shape than will fit neatly on a TV screen. This means that you are left with an 'empty' space in your picture; you either have too much sky in the shot, or too much foreground. Of course, using a panning shot can help avoid this problem, but this technique can seem forced if overused. Whether you are in open countryside with panoramas all around, or in a city, with wide buildings at every corner, you need to find some other way of using the image area efficiently.

The trick here is to try and find something to help fill the empty space. This not only helps fill the unused space, but it also helps create a feeling of depth in the picture.

One of the simplest techniques for doing this is to use what TV cameramen call 'dingle'. By changing your viewpoint slightly, you can usually find a branch of a tree, or a flower, which can block out a significant amount of this wasted space. Flowers, in season, are particularly useful as they add a splash of colour to the frame as well. In order to make sure that they fill a disproportionate amount of space, you will need to get down low, so that the flowers are much closer to the camera than the subject itself.

It doesn't usually matter if the flowers are out of focus, because of limited depth of field – they are only there to help the composition. If you do want them to be identified, you could use a focus pull, where you start recording with the flowers in focus then manually refocus the lens on your main subject whilst recording. In bright light, depth of field will probably not be a problem anyway, and you should be able to get foreground and your subject in sharp focus. Remember, however, to make sure that the subject is sharp – a blurred building, with a sharp daisy in the foreground, will not look impressive.

Often you will find that by looking around you don't have to stretch to using vegetation to fill the foreground. There may be a gate, a dry-stone wall, or a boulder which will serve the same purpose. Walk around until you find something that you can use in this way. A small change in camera angle is all that is usually needed.

With low subjects, such as a bed of flowers, you can end up with a shot where there is no emphasis to your picture. The solution here is to use the subject itself to fill the foreground. Crouch down low, close to the subject, and let the plants dominate the foreground. Plants that are further away will then fill the background.

1: In this shot of a stately home and garden, the lawn could have filled half the picture. By moving slightly to the side, it is possible to frame up the building with 'dingle' in the foreground – on this occasion provided by the magnolia bush.

2–3: In the shot below the symmetrical composition of this palace and formal garden may suit the subject matter, but there is a lot of empty space in the foreground because of the gravel path. For the alternative shot on the left, the camera has moved closer and to the side, and has used the fountain to fill the foreground.

4–5: In these two shots the camera has been positioned low to the ground and very close to the subject itself. This has meant that the cacti and the water lilies have filled the foreground area, so that there is no wasted space in the composition.

Creating Depth

Whilst filling the foreground in some shots can help avoid having unsightly, empty space on screen, the same technique can be used for a completely different purpose. As with photography, video is a two-dimensional medium describing a three-dimensional world. This means that it can be hard to tell anything about depth and distance in our shots.

The only way that the viewers can interpret this third dimension is through their own experience. We know the rough sizes of some of the things we see on screen, and because of this can work out the approximate distances of what we see, and we can guess at the sizes of those objects we have not seen before.

The video operator should therefore try to provide a feeling of depth to his or her shots by including this sort of information in the composition. One of the easiest ways of doing this is to include objects with a recognizable size in the foreground of the image.

The techniques for doing this are much the same as described on the previous page. But here the purpose is to create a feeling of depth on the two-dimensional TV screen. Flowers, boulders, and over-hanging branches again provide exactly what we need.

Another technique to use here is the 'frame within a frame' approach to composition. A doorway, for instance, will not only provide a natural frame for a shot, but it will also add detail to the foreground giving the needed sense of depth. Gateways and doorways can be used in the same way. Even a pair of trees with branches dipping into the top of the frame can be used in this way. The sense of looking through something in this way is one of the most effective ways of creating the missing third dimension on a TV screen.

1: By including the yellow flowers in a dominant position in the foreground of this shot, the viewer is given enough information to work out the approximate size of this impressive garden statue.

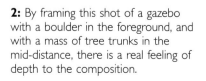

2: By framing this shot of a gazebo with a boulder in the foreground, and with a mass of tree trunks in the mid-distance, there is a real feeling of depth to the composition.

3: Using a doorway as a natural frame not only adds foreground interest to the shot, but also conveys depth and distance to the viewer.

4: Here a bough of a tree is used as a natural frame, helping the viewer to appreciate the depth of this picturesque garden.

Dutch Tilts

A Dutch tilt is a very simple technique which can make some rather ordinary shots look more interesting. The essence of the trick is that the camera is turned slightly on its side, so that horizontal lines become diagonals.

It's a well-known fact of photographic composition that diagonal lines look more dynamic than horizontal or vertical ones. And stills photographers will often tilt their cameras to strengthen the composition in this way.

One subject where the use of Dutch tilts has become a cliché is when shooting fast or luxury cars. They seem always to be shown at 45 degrees, which not only emphasizes speed and motion, and strengthens the composition, but also means that long cars can be framed up more tightly on screen, with less empty space than with a straight shot.

Dutch tilts also work well when videoing modern buildings, especially skyscrapers. Buildings are never easy to video as there is no movement. Tall buildings are even harder as you cannot even keep things at ground level in the frame. A tilted shot, however, can again make the composition tighter, and more dynamic.

You'll find that video tripods do not normally allow you to move the head in this plane, so if you want things on a slant you will need to make one of the legs of the tripod shorter than the others.

1: Shooting at a 45-degree angle makes this shot of a luxury sports car look more dynamic.

2: A Dutch tilt is often the perfect answer for getting decent-looking shots of modern buildings.

The Wedding Video

Thorough planning is the keystone to making a good video, and involves visualizing the event which you are about to cover. First, think about the nature of the location and the lighting conditions you can expect to find there, and ways of overcoming any potential problems. Then consider how the nature of the event will affect your treatment. In the wedding project covered in this chapter – something which most people with a camcorder are likely to be asked to cover – there is no chance for a second take. Everything must go right on the big day – for the couple and for you.

Wedding Checklist

Wedding of ....

Date ....

INITIAL COVERAGE

VENUE (eg BRIDE'S HOME) ....

TIME ALLOWED ....

COVERAGE OF CEREMONY

VENUE OF CEREMONY ....

TRANSPORT DETAILS

Distance to Venue	Time for Travel	Traffic Report

TIME GUESTS ARRIVE ....

TIME BRIDE ARRIVES ....

TIME CEREMONY BEGINS ....

IS FILMING PERMITTED DURING CEREMONY? ....

TIME CEREMONY ENDS ....

COVERAGE AFTER CEREMONY

_____

_____

_____

_____

_____

_____

_____

COVERAGE OF RECEPTION

VENUE OF RECEPTION . . . .

TRANSPORT DETAILS

Distance to Venue   Time for Travel

TIME WEDDING PARTY/RECEPTION EXPECTED TO END . . . .

SPECIAL COVERAGE REQUIREMENTS

_____

_____

PEOPLE

BRIDE   GROOM
BRIDESMAIDS   ATTENDANTS

BEST MAN

BRIDE'S PARENTS   GROOM'S PARENTS

OTHER GUESTS

_____   _____   _____   _____

_____   _____   _____   _____

_____   _____   _____   _____

_____   _____   _____   _____

TELEPHONE NUMBERS

BRIDE'S FAMILY   RECEPTION VENUE
CEREMONY VENUE   OTHERS

EQUIPMENT REQUIREMENTS

☐ CAMCORDER AND ACCESSORIES   ☐ TAPES

☐ BATTERIES   ☐ OTHER EQUIPMENT

Planning Coverage

The ceremony is only one element of the wedding day, the reception and the departure of the bride and groom being further high points that you will need to cover. The latter will provide many excellent opportunities to take informal shots of family and friends to complement the set-piece sequences. You should also discuss in advance which relatives and friends the couple want you to concentrate on. It may help if together you take a look at old family albums to enable you to recognize such key characters on the day.

One important consideration at this stage in your planning is whether you are going to edit after shooting. If you are, you will have much greater flexibility in terms of coverage – poor material can therefore be cut out and interesting sequences juxtaposed with one another. If this is the case, remember to include a lead-in time of about five seconds on each shot.

However, without editing facilities, everything you shoot will appear in the same sequence on the finished tape. Therefore note how long each sequence you intend covering might last, and stick to this schedule when it comes to the actual shoot. This not only adds an element of structure to the video, but also prevents you from running out of tape at a crucial moment.

If you have allowed for a recording time of one hour, plan for the coverage to last about 50 minutes, so that you have 10 minutes to include extra off-the-cuff footage. In general, this should be quite long enough to cover all the main elements of the event, as well as being short enough to avoid repetition and retain audience attention. Remember that your battery is likely to give up before you get to the end of a tape.

1: Coverage of the bride's preparations for the big day makes a good introduction to the tape. Make sure, though, that she includes you in her schedule. The old saying 'something old, something new, something borrowed, something blue' could make a good theme for this part of the video.

2: When the bride and groom really go to town on their transport, it is essential to catch the pomp of their arrival. In covering such a scene, begin in long-shot and move into close-up on the bride's face – she, after all, is the star of the day. Catch the reaction of friends and family as the bride arrives.

3–4: The kiss is another high point that should be included in your coverage. Don't try competing with the official stills photographer for such shots, but discuss with him at the start of the day the best means of getting the right people together at a suitable time.

5: Formal groups can appear static on video, so such coverage should not be extensive. This scene, taken from a slightly high angle, establishes the background and the atmosphere of the reception.

6–7: At the reception, it is possible to get informal shots of the guests enjoying themselves. By moving in close and seeming to become part of the celebrations, you may find people respond well to the camera, instead of shying away from it.

The Right Start

Even with such an apparently relatively straight-forward project as a wedding video, it is important to treat it with the same professionalism as any other project. Your first concern must be to grab your audience's attention.

An opening shot of the bride makes a fine start, and the way in which you deal with this sequence will, to an extent, set the tone and pace of the tape. For example, if you shoot the chaotic preparations in the bride's house, with all the last-minute checks and setbacks, the initial feel would be one of hurry and bustle. You could, at this stage, incorporate some amusing, candid shots such as the principal characters desperately searching for the elusive wedding ring, flowers and buttonholes! Such sequences have the added advantage of informally introducing the most important members of the two families. This part of the tape will interestingly and dramatically contrast with the formal ceremony which follows. If you choose such an opening sequence, devote about 10 minutes to it. Any more and the video audience will grow impatient for the bride's departure to the church.

An alternative would be to create a gentler, more reflective approach, emphasizing the impor-tance of the day. An opening shot of the bride alone in her room, sadly taking a last look at the images of a life which she is about to leave behind, could be highly effective. This could be shot earlier in the week when everything is less hectic. You could develop this theme by following up with shots of the bride's parents discussing the reception plans and giving their daughter encouragement and moral support for the events of the coming big day.

In many ways the choice of treatment depends on the bride's personality. The first approach would be more appropriate to an extrovert; the latter to someone who is more introspective. In either case, discuss the options first. And finally, remember that the last thing the bride or groom wants in the nervous hours before the wedding is you interrupting proceedings by telling them what to do in order to get a particular shot.

You may not be able to wait for the bride's departure from the house, as you must be at the church early to shoot the arrival of the guests, and for shots of a worried groom and hassled best man. Leave plenty of time to get to the church, to allow for any unexpected hold-ups or to solve any problems that face you when you arrive.

2–3: Luckily, a fast car can beat a horse-drawn coach any day, so it was not difficult to record the bride's departure from her house and get to the church in time to set up the camera for her arrival.

1: An opening sequence of the bride taking a last look around her home. The framing against the mirror brings additional interest to the shot.

4: As an opening shot this breaks with the tradition of the groom not seeing the bride until she reaches the altar. It does, however, have the advantage of showing the two main characters at the outset.

7–8: While you should make sure that you get coverage of the guests enjoying themselves, don't neglect the bride and groom during the reception. Be on the look out for candid coverage which reveals their quieter moments together.

5–6: Following the ceremony, the next part of the coverage is the reception. This could be introduced by shots of the couple together, emphasizing the idea of marriage. An alternative, suggested here by the Edwardian dress of the guests, would be to arrange formal poses to introduce family members.

9: The high angle used to record this formal group distances the subject from the audience. The camera panned to include the reactions of other guests watching the official photography.

Practical Considerations

It is easy to forget the practicalities of making a video in the heat of trying to achieve your planned coverage without missing anything.

Inside the church, you will probably have set focus manually – this usually produces a sharper image, and is relatively simple in a formal situation in which the subjects do not move from one position to another. (For coverage of the bridge coming down the aisle, you should have rehearsed your positions and each focus on your exploratory visit to the church.)

At the reception, your coverage will be more informal and it is probably best to rely on the camera's autofocus to get the shots right.

Lighting is another matter. In the project shown here, the reception took place outside on a glorious afternoon with the sun beating down. But these otherwise excellent weather conditions can cause problems of exposure (if possible, take a test recording beforehand). For example, too much glare from the white tablecloth when you use auto exposure will create problems. Also note that the auto exposure often adjusts too much, leaving other elements in the scene bleached out as it tries to compensate for extremely bright features in the foreground. You may find that by setting the exposure manually you can get better results.

You should also beware of shooting directly into the sun – this is not an occasions to take risks with adventurous lighting. Again, the automatic backlight control, if used, may overcorrect the exposure in very bright conditions. Stick to having the light behind you for the most important shots so that the automatic exposure system does not have any such problems.

3: Bright sunlight doesn't just cause problems for the camera operator. Everyone at the wedding party was feeling the heat, but ties remained the order of the day!

4: If the light is good you can safely rely on autofocus to see you through the afternoon's proceedings. But indoors you may have to watch the white balance, and may find manual focus more reliable.

1: In strong sunlight, avoid shooting directly into the sun or deep shade. It is very easy to lose an important face in the shadows if you use adventurous lighting on such an occasion.

2: Full sunlight on a brilliant white tablecloth can result in exposure problems. If your camcorder has no way of overriding the exposure, you will have to reframe the shot so that the problem (here, the tablecloth) is no longer in the picture.

Further Coverage

The reception or wedding party is your opportunity to talk to the guests and ask them for reminiscences of the bride and groom.

Try to act as a participant in the wedding feast yourself – you will be far more likely to get interesting comments from other guests if you approach in a friendly, conversational manner. Although the bride and groom may not want anecdotes of their childhood revealed, they are sure to be told and you could make amusing inserts of such stories.

Don't forget the older, more retiring members of the party, and remember that children will provide an interesting change of pace. When talking to them, remember to crouch down to their level, this not only puts them more at ease but will also give you the best camera angle.

Set pieces don't just include the main events of the day, but also smaller, equally highly prized moments, such as the reading of telegrams and letters of congratulations. Such moments are an important ritual, as is the tradition of the bride and groom cutting the cake.

The final event of the day that you must be sure to cover is the departure of the bride and groom, when the former will toss the bridal bouquet. Be sure to provide a close-up of the delighted face of whoever catches it. And make sure that the groom's best man lets you know in good time when the couple intend to slip away.

1–2: Since the best man will be the groom's closest friend, and has a key role in the day's proceedings, it is vital that you feature him in the video, ideally with the groom. Note how in recording this sequence the extreme sunlight and shade has caused exposure problems. Try to keep your subjects in evenly lit areas to avoid these difficulties.

3: Keep an eye out for children at the reception, especially when they get away from the adults. Children can add charm and humour to your coverage of the reception. See how these three were entirely engrossed in their own conversation and completely unaware of the presence of the camera.

4: Children are less intimidated by the camera when you get down to their own level. Ask them about their impressions of the day, whether or not they liked the food, or if they intend to get married, in order to draw them out and, hopefully, to get some amusing answers.

5: The bride and groom departing by carriage. Coverage of this moment should include long-shots to show the overall scene, as well as close-ups of individual guests identified earlier in the day.

Timing Sequences

One of the difficult choices to make when covering the wedding reception is to decide how long your coverage should last. If you are unable to edit, you will probably have allocated something like 20 minutes, but the set pieces (such as cutting the cake and the speeches) will take up most of that time. This leaves you with little space for interviews with family and friends. It is also easy to get carried away and record almost continuously, thus losing a sense of structure in the tape.

In fact, it is far better to be selective about your coverage and to limit the sequences that you record to quite short chunks. When you ask friends to say something about the bride and groom, a few short sentences are more effective than a long, meandering monologue.

Similarly, coverage of people eating and drinking becomes rather tedious to watch after a while. By shooting in 10-second bursts at regular intervals, you convey more visual interest and indicate the passing of time through the course of the afternoon. This also allows you to relax and to integrate more fully into the celebrations, and that in turn will make the coverage that you get more relaxed and lively.

As long as you remain alert to the major moments of the afternoon, you will be able to produce a video which accurately reflects the atmosphere of the bride and groom's big day and gives great pleasure to everyone involved.

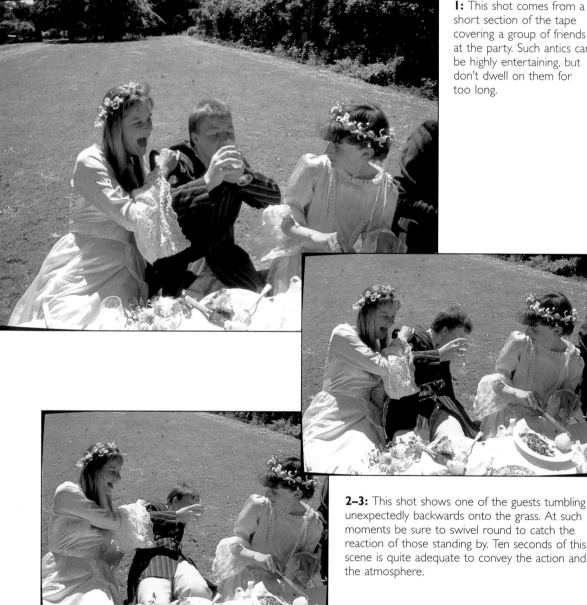

1: This shot comes from a short section of the tape covering a group of friends at the party. Such antics can be highly entertaining, but don't dwell on them for too long.

2–3: This shot shows one of the guests tumbling unexpectedly backwards onto the grass. At such moments be sure to swivel round to catch the reaction of those standing by. Ten seconds of this scene is quite adequate to convey the action and the atmosphere.

4: This shot is of the bride-groom responding to the telegrams and speeches. If possible, record the speeches using an external microphone placed centrally on the table (it can easily be hidden). Nearby sound, such as guests clapping, will be over-prominent using the in-camera microphone.

5–6: Your coverage should reflect the fun of the wedding party as much as it did the formality of the ceremony. The exchange of kisses and hugs after the speeches is shown here.

Cutaways

If you are going to edit your coverage after shooting, then you do not have to be so selective about the coverage and timing of your material. Any shots that do not work can be discarded, and over-lengthy sequences can be cut down to a more manageable size.

With editing you can also introduce cutaway shots, which are not central to the main action in the sequence, into your video. Such material, for example, could be of someone trying not to fall asleep while speeches are being made, or of a young child abandoning the banquet to prowl beneath the dining table amidst a forest of legs. Such material could, of course, be captured without editing, but they need to be kept short – a few

seconds at the very most. If you are going to edit, remember that cutaways should have a five-second or so lead-in time to facilitate editing – they can be pruned to length later.

Repeated cutaways can add a second, subsidiary storyline to the tape. For example, if the camera goes back to shots of the dining table throughout the afternoon, this acts both as a record of the guests congregating at this focal point, and also signals time passing as we see the plates gradually being emptied of food. Other cutaways can be used to keep track of interesting characters.

Remember the golden rule – keep them to two or three seconds. Otherwise, the effect will tend to diminish.

1–2: Cutaway shots around the table can isolate individual guests in conversation. Use them to convey the general sense of animation and conviviality at the wedding party, but don't allow the coverage to become too unstructured. Never lose sight of the main theme of the sequence.

3: Keep a look out for spontaneous action. Such light-hearted moments are not central to the day's events, but they do convey the happy mood of the occasion.

4: Cutaways don't necessarily have to be in close-up. In fact, if the main part of the sequence is filmed in close-up or mid-shot, cutaways are often more effective in long-shot.

5: By their informal nature, cutaway shots should not be posed. This shot would be a perfect cutaway to insert into a wedding speech when it comes to editing the footage, showing the girl's reaction to one of the jokes.

Moving Camera Shots

The golden rule in video is to let the action happen in front of the camera, not to let the camera chase the action. However, shots of the reception in progress taken from a fixed camera position could easily seem rather static, compared with the liveliness of the event, although this can be overcome to a considerable extent by changing camera positions when new shots are required.

Despite this general rule, you could indulge in some camera movement. The most successful of these shots will be when the camera moves around and across the action it is recording – *crabbing* is the term for sideways movement, *arcing* when the camera moves around a subject. Such shots allow the viewer to observe the subject from different viewpoints and to place him or her within the broader context of the scene. The crabbing movement should be slow, and the camera should remain at a constant distance from the subject. In this sense it differs from the pan: the pan introduces new material into the frame; while the crab shot shows the same material from a new angle.

The arcing shot is also useful when recording moving subjects. If someone is walking towards the camera, you can move slowly to the side so that the shot ends with them walking away from the camera. Whilst the arcing shot is useful in varying your coverage, use it with moderation.

1: The arcing action is one in which the camera makes a circular sweep around the subject. It can be used on any shot – close-up, mid-shot or long-shot. Keep the image size constant, however – combining an arcing shot with one in which the size of the image within the frame changes does not work.

2–4: The arcing shot around the guest wearing the bowler hat also includes the other guest carving the ham. The two subjects are placed in relationship by the moving camera. This type of shot shows off the work that has gone into the preparation of the food and flowers, as well as including guests which otherwise might not be featured prominently in the video.

Range of Coverage

Although you should do as much advance planning for every shoot as you possibly can, you should not approach your video making with too many preconceptions about exactly what is going to happen.

There are bound to be certain sequences that you will want to capture, and that the bride and groom will want you to record. And of course you should go all out to film these. But this should not blind you to the other opportunities for coverage that you may not be able to plan. Be alert for these at all times and you will produce a video with the right mixture of the expected and the spontaneous.

The shots on this page come from a wedding video that illustrated this blend very well. There were plenty of predictable sequences – such as shots of the bride before she left home, and cover-

age of the couple immediately after the ceremony. But there were also surprises – the colourful guard of honour with musical accompaniment, and the unexpected telegrams with their humorous messages. Both these scenes were gifts to the video maker, adding colour, movement and amusement, as well as providing plenty of chances for the video to capture the surprised reactions of the guests to the various happenings. It is often these 'added extras' that make a video truly memorable.

There are always a lot of little touches that go to make a good wedding. Each one has taken someone hours of preparation, but which can so easily be forgotten. Brief close-up shots of the bouquets, the rings, the order of service and so on, are always worth shooting. These can also provide you with very useful cutaways, or visual breaks, whilst editing.

3–4: The unexpected – whether ceremonial or simply humorous – will add variety and a little light relief. Even small touches which have made the day that bit more special can be recorded to be used as cutaways at the editing stage.

1–2: Shots like these of the bride and the couple might seem predictable, but people will expect to see them in a wedding video.

Project Notebook

WEDDINGS

These project notebooks (there is one at the end of every chapter in the book) are designed to offer an informal *résumé* of some of the ideas that have been introduced and to pinpoint some of the problems that have already been encountered. Since the range of video experience is as exhaustive as the range of subjects that you may choose to cover, no book can be comprehensive. Make your own notes about techniques, situations, and problems encountered and solved as you go along. Such a record will be as invaluable as the experience you gain from tackling different projects as you explore the world of video.

■ The manual might say: Turn up, turn on, point and shoot – it's as easy as that. Experience proves, after the first few shots, that there is no substitute for planning the shoot in advance.

■ Planning that is not carried out in detail is as bad as no planning at all.

■ Video is a combination of art and practicalities: the composition of the interior shot might look great, but are you sure that the autofocus system has locked onto the subject correctly?

■ When you've got a great exterior location for a series of shots, it always rains – make contingency plans, just in case.

■ Think coverage first, sequences second, shots next.

■ People are not robots, they don't run to time or to orders.

■ Don't be obtrusive: mix and be friendly. Let others enjoy and enjoy yourself.

■ Shoot lots of close-ups of smiling faces, of flowers, and people reacting to the speeches. These can be very useful at the editing stage to help smooth the joins – but do keep them as short as possible.

Working with People

The basic unit of the language of video is the 'shot', which should contain sufficient information for the viewer to understand what is going on at any particular point in the narrative. But shots should be more than informative, they should be pleasing to look at too.

This chapter – which concentrates on videos of people, from footage of the family to more highly structured interviews – examines some of the basic rules for composing such shots. But while many of the principles are the same as in stills photography, there will be additional techniques to master.

Camera Angles

If you watch television, you'll notice that most shots of people are taken from shoulder level and frame the subject with a long-shot. Mid-shots and close-ups are used for more intimate situations, such as interviews, or shots which record the reaction of the subject to something that has happened earlier in the narrative. While the significance of these different types of shot has already been considered, note how the position of the camera also has an effect on the way the viewer 'reads' the image.

The most obvious camera angles are the low- and high-angle shots, which are shot from below or above the subject. These immediately imply a sense of either inferiority or superiority. This can be used to imply certain relationships between characters: for example if, in an interview, the subject is shown from a slightly low angle, he or she naturally assumes a greater authority on the screen. This is because the audience automatically identifies with the shot, and subconsciously agrees with its point of view. Of course, if the camera angle is too low, the shot will instead appear odd, and the psychological effect will be lost.

Camera angles also help to establish a sense of space within the screen and create a more satisfying sense of composition. A head-on shot of a character gives the viewer little sense of depth. But by placing the camera at 45 degrees to the subject, elements of the background are more fully integrated into the frame. In general, shots taken from such an angle are seen as 'neutral' – the camera is regarded as an observer of the scene, rather than an active participant, as is implied by a head-on shot.

Extreme camera angles call attention to themselves, and should only be used if your intention is to convey a sense of the extraordinary. In film and television, they tend to be used for suspense or shock effects. So, if you use a similar extreme angle for an everyday event, such as an elderly person recalling their childhood, you will inadvertently imply that there is either something very unusual about this, or the shot will just look odd.

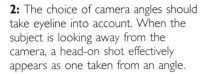

1: Shots of children are too often taken from an 'adult' high-angle level. By bending down, and shooting from a slightly lower angle, the individuality of the child is given more emphasis.

2: The choice of camera angles should take eyeline into account. When the subject is looking away from the camera, a head-on shot effectively appears as one taken from an angle.

3–4: The high-angle shot above works better than the one on the right. Because the camera is immediately above the children it looks more intimate, whilst in the shot on the right we can't even see the children's faces.

5–6: Note how by following the rules of composition this shot could have been improved. The head appearing at the bottom left-hand corner of the shot (**5**) distracts the audience's attention and disrupts the composition. The solution is to move in that little bit closer and exclude it.

Balanced Composition

The basic rules of composing the shot are very similar to those that govern composition in stills photography. However, the frame area that you have to work with is that of the television screen, an area four units in width by three in depth. Unlike with photographs, you can't crop the picture, or even take upright shots.

The first consideration is that the subject should be framed centrally on the screen. The screen area allows little room for freedom – its edges command scant attention from the viewer. If a subject is framed too low, it will give the impression that it is 'dropping out' of the screen.

Close-up shots should be framed at head and shoulders, rather than head and neck. In fact, there are a number of cut-off points on the body that are best avoided – the knees in a long-shot and the waist in mid-shot. For big close-ups, frame the subject from the chin upwards, allowing the top of the head to project just out of the top of the screen. When taking long-shots of people, allow a space between the feet and the bottom of the screen. It looks odd if the subject appears to be walking along the bottom of the frame.

The purpose behind all framing techniques is first to concentrate the viewers' attention on the main subject and, second, to achieve a visually pleasing image on the screen. The first objective is achieved by framing centrally, while the second requires a good deal of thought about the elements within the frame.

In addition to the subject, the frame will also contain elements in the foreground and background. By cleverly using foreground elements you can suggest that we are spying on the main subject. A clichéd example of this involves the camera lens peeping through foliage, which is visible round the edges of the screen. Such framing gives an interesting sense of depth to the shot. The technique can be extended by focusing first on the foreground and then using the zoom to concentrate on the subject. This gives you the best of both worlds – the context together with detailed coverage of the subject itself. But be careful not to overuse the zoom with this technique.

The background elements help the viewer to place the subject of the shot within its context. But when framing subjects in close-up be careful that you do not omit the background. It is usually better to frame the subject in mid-shot, allowing the viewer to take in the background, and then slowly move in for a close-up.

1–2: The two shots above show how small changes in framing can have considerable effect on the image. Shot 1 fills the frame and looks balanced. Shot 2 is off-centre and the viewers' attention is distracted by what is happening in the background.

3–4: The head-on shot on the left is less successful in video than in stills photography, partly because the subjects become too conscious of the camera. The side-on shot of the two girls, above, is much more relaxed and natural.

In and Out of the Frame

Since video is about moving images, framing techniques must also take motion into account. Many shots will be of people or vehicles moving from one location to another. In such shots it is necessary to leave 'lead space'. This means that subjects should be placed to one side of the screen, leaving up to two-thirds of the screen area for them to move into. Without this lead space, subjects appear to be too contained by the borders of the screen.

A further convention on framing moving subjects is that they should move diagonally across the screen so avoiding the head-on shot which draws too much attention to the camera.

An extension of this convention applies to entering and leaving the screen area. The diagonal rule states that subjects should not enter or exit the frame from the sides of the screen. To the viewer, this again looks as if the subject is 'falling out' of the shot. Whilst subjects can enter the shot from any direction, they should first appear at the corners of the screen.

When framing moving subjects, there are two basic options. The camera can either follow the subject as it moves, or remain static, allowing the subject to enter and exit the frame.

Following the subject implies that the shot will end at a specific destination. Such shots are best achieved by a tracking and panning action in which the camera moves around the subject, who then exits from the frame moving away from the camera.

There are occasions in which you may require the action to happen head-on. Such movement towards the camera can bring with it an enormous dramatic impact, as happens in so many car chases in feature films. The convention is also used by documentary film makers to imply that the subject is completely unaware of the camera, so lending authenticity to the project.

1: The classic composition of a moving action shot. The subject in long-shot, the road leads diagonally out of the frame, providing lead space for the subject to move into.

2: From a fixed camera position, the subject moves towards the centre of the frame. Once the subject moves beyond this point, the viewer accepts that they are about to leave.

3: Because the action was framed diagonally, the subject exits the frame from the corner of the screen. If you were going to pan with the action, the camera movement should have begun at an earlier point when there was more lead space in the frame.

4: Head-on shots of moving subjects present more immediacy to the viewer. Since there is no movement relative to the frame itself, these shots should be framed centrally.

5: As the subject comes into close-up, the diagonal rule of entering and exiting the screen applies. The diagonal line here is given by the subject's eyeline.

6: A scene from a panning shot. The subject is given lead space in which to move. This space should be kept throughout the pan. If this were a static camera shot, the subject would appear to enter and exit from the sides of the screen – an obtrusive shot for audiences.

7: The pan ends with the camera coming to rest. The subject naturally exits from the shot in the far distance.

Setting up an Interview

Interviews require two separate skills: those which establish the character of the interviewee and the camera skills which provide the best coverage of the interview.

Interviewing skills grow out of good research. Unless you have a detailed knowledge of your subject, it's unlikely you will ask the right questions, or give the interview with any structure or purpose. Obviously, the nature of this research depends on your subject matter. Many public figures have had extensive press coverage which you can examine in libraries and newspaper files. But preparing an interview with someone who has attracted comparatively little press attention means that you will have to do your own homework. Without such research you will be in danger of asking non-questions, or of concentrating on side issues so leaving your viewers frustrated as they wait for you to tackle the main issues.

Apart from exceptional occasions your main concern will be to put your subject at ease. This means that you must be relaxed in front of the camera, otherwise your nervousness will quickly 'infect' your subject. To further relax him or her, you might reveal beforehand the questions you will be asking, though this approach might lead

to stilted, set-piece replies. Its great advantage, however, is that your subject will have had time to consider the questions and, therefore, will be able to give fuller replies.

Avoid asking questions which can be answered with either a 'yes' or 'no'. Instead, introduce topics on which the interviewee can expand. Don't so concentrate on your next question that you either miss responding to what's being said, or ignore an unexpected opportunity to discuss other interesting subjects. Nor should you go to the other extreme, relentlessly interrupting. The viewer wants to hear your subject's opinions, not yours.

Camera technique will also be determined by the nature of the interview. In the project shown here, the subject kept a unique private zoo specializing in South American birds and animals, so obviously the background was very important. (In other situations, coverage would be kept very much to mid-shots and close-ups of the interviewer and the interviewee.) If you are able to edit your coverage afterwards, concentrate on filming your subject. You can shoot the interviewer putting questions and responding afterwards, and insert this footage at appropriate points in the edited tape.

1: The opening shots of the interview should establish the background in which it takes place. In this case, the colourful interior of the subject's house provided interesting material in its own right.

2: The over-the-shoulder shot is useful for establishing the subject's immediate reaction to a question. However, if the shot lasts too long, the presence of the interviewer's back on screen becomes irritating and distracting.

3: In an informal interview, most shots can be framed at mid-shot. Close-ups intrude upon the subject and imply that the interview is in fact a dramatic interrogation.

4: Where the situation permits, allow the subject to perform or demonstrate a point. In this case, the animals from Lady Fisher's collection provide an additional source of interest and reveal the interviewee's close relationship with them. In other situations, you could show sequences of the subject at work, or demonstrating, for instance, a particular cooking point. In an interview with a zoo owner, viewers will naturally want to see some of her animals, and in close-up shots.

Interview Shots

Like any other video project, interviews should have a clear, logical structure, with a beginning, middle and end. The piece can be introduced by the interviewer giving a brief outline of the ground that the discussion will cover. Alternatively, you could begin with a long-shot of the interviewer and subject in conversation, gradually moving in to pick up what they are saying.

During the interview there are three basic shots to use in providing coverage. These are a big close-up framed at the chin, a close-up just below the shoulders, and a mid-shot taken at the breast. You can alternate between these shots as the interview progresses, but try to keep the frame size as constant as possible.

Of course, there is no need to restrict yourself to these three shots, but they should provide you with sufficient visual variety. If there are natural pauses or breaks in the interview, they can be emphasized by recommencing with shots taken from a new camera position. The end of an interview can be indicated in two ways. The interviewer can thank his subject for having taken part in the film. And the camera can reinforce the sense of an ending either by resting on the subject or by gradually withdrawing into long-shot.

Below: Three set-ups for interviews. **(i)** has two cameras recording the interviewer and interviewee respectively. With **(ii)**, using the over-the-shoulder technique, both interviewer and subject will be in each shot. The head-on shot **(iii)** is used for a direct speech to camera – when the interviewer introduces the interview, for example.

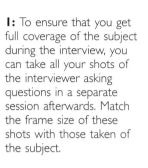

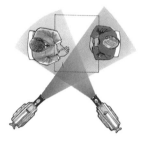

1: To ensure that you get full coverage of the subject during the interview, you can take all your shots of the interviewer asking questions in a separate session afterwards. Match the frame size of these shots with those taken of the subject.

2: The interview is being recorded by a single camera. An experienced interviewer will be aware of the camera's position and make sure that he or she does not obscure the subject.

3: A good opening shot for the interview. The interviewer and subject are seen in a long-shot, framed against the attractive conservatory windows.

Shooting Groups

When shooting groups composition is far more difficult than when framing a single individual. Groups are by their nature rather untidy, and they also tend to suffer from a number of people competing for your camcorder's attention!

A common mistake is for the camera operator to move in too close so as to concentrate on an individual. Unfortunately the temptation is then to keep referring back to this individual, which results in confusing, jerky coverage with too many camera movements.

How you approach different situations will depend on how much control you have over your subjects. For example, a brass band playing in a local park is in a static position, so you can plan your shots from fixed camera positions. With smaller groups you may be able to ask the participants to stand within a particular area, and again you can plan your coverage beforehand, using fixed camera positions.

In formal situations you can even arrange groups to fit a particular composition – smaller members of the group standing in front of larger members, with the major participants located somewhere in the centre of the shot. Usually, a group becomes a crowd when you have little or no control over its actions. Again, the coverage will depend to an extent on the situation. Where crowds are basically static, as in the stands at a sports event, it is easy to isolate individuals. In a busy shopping centre it is far more difficult to pick people out.

In general, crowds should be covered in long-shot. This allows the viewer to place the action within its context, and means that the action can develop in front of the camera. Use slow pans to take in more of the scene, resting on an additional point of interest. If the situation allows, use a tripod, as this will help keep these camera movements smooth and even.

Since the audience will concentrate its attention on the centre of the screen, frame items of particular interest centrally.

If you zoom in on an individual or some other detail, it is usually best not to go in too close since extreme changes of scale tend to appear obtrusive. Such a zoom shot could therefore be followed by a pan before moving back into a long-shot of the scene. In this way your video will have more variety and the audience will not forget the context of the shot – there is an individual there, but he belongs to the crowd.

1: This group scene was easily framed. It was taken in Egypt, with the dusty road and hazy light in the background conveying a strong sense of place. The family group is on its way to a local market. The high key-lighting shows the viewer the hot, dusty conditions.

2: Many people naturally arrange themselves to provide good shots. You will often find that a husband and wife walk together, with their children on either side. Here the exposure has been set to give a silhouette, highlighting this symmetry.

3: The conclusion of a long-shot of a family group. With the camera mounted on a tripod, the subjects move into the far distance.

4: Children playing in the street. The two skipping girls were framed slightly off-centre so that the other children could also be included in the sequence.

3: The long perspective down the street draws the viewer's eyes away from the group in the foreground, sitting at the cafe tables.

4: The same scene from a slightly higher camera position. The viewer gets the impression of looking in on the group – almost of spying. Such an elevated camera position tends to place the audience in a more objective position than one taken at eye level.

1: This group of girls dressed in their bright school uniforms is posed rather self-consciously in front of the camera. But their giggling response to a few questions saved the shot, and made it quite charming.

5: Wherever you go with a camcorder you will become the centre of attention. Most people are curious and amused about being filmed, but some can be resentful. If someone requests you to stop shooting it is prudent as well as polite to comply.

6: You can encourage your subjects to react by moving in closer and picking out individuals from amongst the crowd. Making light-hearted conversation will also help to break the ice and get your subjects to 'perform' for the camcorder.

2: Formal group compositions can work on video. While this group was being posed for a stills photographer, it was clear that the event was actually a marvellous subject for a video sequence.

Creative Framing

The importance of aesthetically pleasing framing has already been discussed. But beyond this, creative framing can add considerably to the meaning of the shot. In fact, the choice of camera angles and the relationship of elements in the shot often amount to a form of directorial style.

It is an instructive exercise to look at film and television productions from a purely technical point of view. Try to estimate where the camera was placed for each particular shot, and notice how long individual shots are held. Although the director usually has the last say about shots, the writer of the script will indicate how he or she has visualized the moment, often quite precisely. The final shot seen on screen will be the result of a collaborative effort of the video crew.

In stills photography, framing can be used as an end in itself. In video, the progress of the narrative comes first, with framing serving to inform the audience of what is going on and then to give some insight into the characters on screen. A typical example of framing adding to the narrative is the classic 'it's behind you' shot that occurs in suspense films. The frame allows the audience to see something in the background while the main characters remain unaware of it.

Framing to imply character often uses slightly high- or low-angle shots. For example, if one character in a drama is usually shown from a high angle from another character's point of view, it implies a sense of superiority. Reverse these camera angles at the conclusion of the drama, when the second character gains dominance, and the psychological impact will be implicitly understood by the audience.

Creative composition makes full use of objects in the foreground and background. Remember that prominent foreground objects will distract the audience from the central characters, so they should lend some significance to the narrative if they are going to be included.

In drama, for example, a compromising letter may lie between the camera and a main character. In a more mundane example, you could place airline tickets in the foreground in an opening shot of a holiday video. Background objects are less prominent, and their significance can be emphasized by a slow zoom in from the main area of action if you want to make a specific point about them. A slow change of focus from foreground to background can help to make a background object more dominant.

1–3: What works as a static image on the page may not do so as video. These shots were taken from an experimental sequence in which a girl moved up and down in front of the stationary camera, causing her head to fall out of the bottom and sides of the screen at times. They just don't work on video.

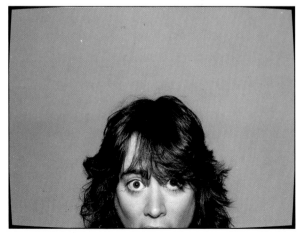

4–5: A full profile on a television screen always looks unnaturally posed, perhaps because in real life we seldom look at people from that angle. Used in a video it gives a distancing effect. Similarly with the lower image: as the three people are all looking in different directions the shot seems extremely forced.

Eyelines

The direction of a subject's gaze on screen is one of the major clues that the viewer uses in order to understand what is happening in the narrative. When in one shot the subject appears to be looking towards the left, the viewer expects the next shot to reveal what the subject is looking at. In this way, eyelines establish the direction of the action and set up a sense of space on screen. This means that when two characters are talking on screen, they must be shown looking in opposite directions – so that they are still facing each other when shown individually in close-up.

The video camera can imitate the angle of the character's gaze as well as direction. If one person is seated, then a point-of-view shot from that position should be taken from a low angle. This effect can be a useful ally when you want the audience to identify strongly with one particular character.

Where there is little action happening on screen, eyelines can provide the missing connection between the characters. Viewers usually concentrate on screen characters' faces, and therefore follow the direction in which they are looking. This means that eyelines can be used as a powerful tool when planning the composition of relatively static shots.

When there are more than two characters involved in the on-screen action, the eyeline becomes more complex. In such situations, the direction of gaze can establish a number of separate eyelines, linking different characters in different relationships: the eyeline between A and B, B and C, A and C, and so on. Depending on what action unfolds, any of these established eyelines may be dominant in a scene. And as the action develops, and the characters move to different positions, so these eyelines will change.

It is possible to become over-obsessed about complex eyelines. A useful approach is to sketch out eyelines while drawing up the storyboard. This at least helps you to have a clear idea in your mind about the priorities for that particular scene, and will help you position characters correctly when it comes to arranging the shot.

Remember, it is the direction of the eyeline from one shot to the next that is important in terms of how the audience interprets screen geography, and unless you think about this clearly while shooting you may run into problems at the editing stage. A sudden cut in which the direction of one character's eyeline changes radically is bound to be noticeable.

1: The eyelines encountered in a shot like this are relatively simple. If the couple in the background are then shown in close-up and turn to face the third character, this will be readily understood by the audience, but if by changing the camera position they appear to face in the opposite direction, the audience will be misled.

2: No problems over eyeline with this particular shot. But if the father were to look to the right, the audience would follow his eyeline and expect the next shot to reveal what he is looking at.

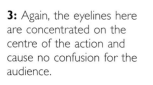

3: Again, the eyelines here are concentrated on the centre of the action and cause no confusion for the audience.

4: In this scene a number of eyelines have been established between characters and groups. When moving in to close-up so as to record characters' reactions, it is easy to disrupt the sense of geography if the eyelines are not thought about.

Frames within Frames

The video image can gain extra visual interest by framing subjects within naturally occurring frames. The most obvious example of this is the framing of subjects within doorways. The strong horizontal and vertical lines of the doorway give a powerful sense of composition to the total image. Such shots will make the viewer look at them more closely, almost as if the shot were a painting.

In many cases such shots will also contain strong lighting contrasts, since the doorway will either be in shade, or backlit if the shot is taken from the interior. Such contrasts add to the atmosphere of the shot, emphasizing the isolation of a character, or suggesting mystery or suspense.

Of course, doorways are not the only internal frames available. Try composing scenes through car windows, with window outline forming a second frame inside the boundaries of the television screen. This can often also serve as a point-of-view shot – the audience recognizes the shot as the view seen by the car's occupant. Most scenes offer some naturally occurring frame which you can use creatively in this way suggesting that the scene is being observed from a particular point of view.

Frames can also be used to add depth to a scene – helping to give that missing third dimension to your TV shots – and they can help fill uninteresting foregrounds when, say, shooting landscapes.

1–2: A good frame gives information about the subject. These dilapidated buildings provoke interest in and sympathy for their occupants.

3: This magnificent staircase is given added grandeur by being framed within the foreground archway. The strong contrast between background and foreground also leads the viewer's attention to the lighter area of the screen.

4: A shady archway with sunlight beyond excite our expectations – what is the courtyard like and who is there?

5: Bridges form good frames for boats. They are also interesting subjects in their own right.

Art on Video

Video is the ideal medium for recording artists and craftsmen and -women at work, since the tape can be instantly reviewed to check that full coverage was obtained. If the subject isn't satisfied with what has been recorded, you can quickly arrange another session.

There are two basic options as far as camera-work is concerned. You may choose to mount the camera on a tripod in front of the subject, using the zoom to go in for close-ups of the subject's face, or of the hands at work. The static coverage allows the audience to concentrate on what the subject is actually doing.

On the other hand, you could choose a roaming-camera, documentary-style approach. Some subjects may be put more at ease by this less formal method of working.

It is a good idea to preface the tape with some background material. This might include a short interview with the artist, in which he or she explains the intentions behind the work. A short guided tour of the studio also makes interesting coverage, and the subject can explain the functions of the different tools and materials used later in the demonstration.

While the artist is actually working, encourage him or her to explain what is going on, going into detail over any particular problems encountered. The tape could conclude with the finished product shown in close-up from different angles.

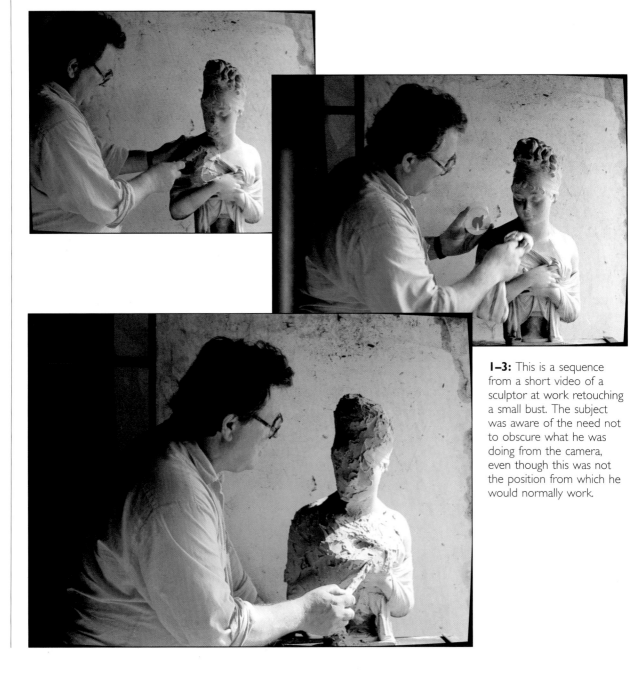

1–3: This is a sequence from a short video of a sculptor at work retouching a small bust. The subject was aware of the need not to obscure what he was doing from the camera, even though this was not the position from which he would normally work.

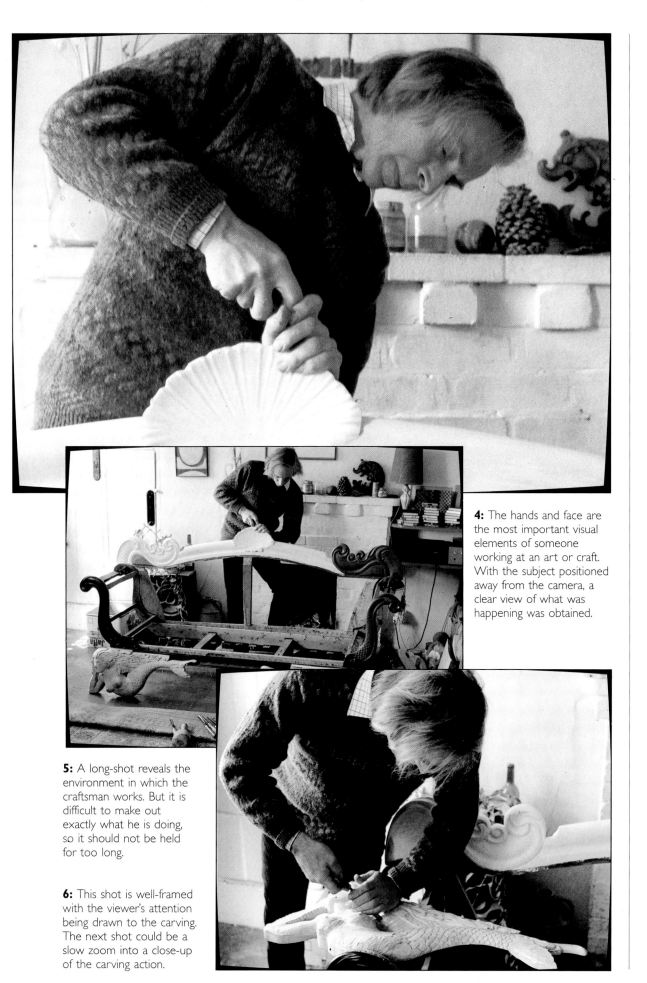

4: The hands and face are the most important visual elements of someone working at an art or craft. With the subject positioned away from the camera, a clear view of what was happening was obtained.

5: A long-shot reveals the environment in which the craftsman works. But it is difficult to make out exactly what he is doing, so it should not be held for too long.

6: This shot is well-framed with the viewer's attention being drawn to the carving. The next shot could be a slow zoom into a close-up of the carving action.

Project Notebook

PEOPLE

Composition of the image within the frame is the technique in which practice meets that of stills photography. The important difference to remember, though, is that video images are moving images, and you must take into account the beginning *and* end of any given sequence. A pleasing, relaxed composition on screen allows the audience to concentrate on what is being shown, rather than being distracted by clumsy, or over-fussy camera techniques.

■ The viewer's attention is drawn irresistibly to the subject's eyes and automatically follows the direction of his or her gaze.

■ Keep a social distance. Human beings don't conduct conversations at extreme distances, nor do they like their personal space invaded. Mid-shots and close-ups are safe. Extreme close-ups imply interrogation.

■ Let the action happen in front of the camera. Keep the camera in the same place unless you have a definite reason for changing the angle.

■ Horizontal and vertical movements within the frame look wrong. Think diagonals.

■ People get nervous in front of a camera. Time spent chatting to your subject, demonstrating how the camcorder works, will help your subjects relax and help you to achieve a more natural result.

■ If you don't research in depth, you won't be able to ask the right questions in an interview.

■ Wherever possible, involve subjects in the whole video project. You should also ensure that they are given the chance to view the finished tape.

Shots and Sequences

The shot may be the basic unit of the 'language' of video, but unless it is related to further images it tells the viewer very little. This chapter is therefore concerned with the techniques for turning shots into sequences.

Sequences are the vital ingredient for giving a video pace and rhythm, and also help establish the growing momentum of the story being filmed. They can be short or long, from a few seconds to a few minutes, depending on the effect you wish to create. Most of the sequences in this chapter are taken from an informal record of a summer holiday.

Holiday Action

Holidays are not all sitting around the poolside, or on the beach. For many, they give the opportunity to try a number of interesting and exciting sports, such as windsurfing, snorkelling or hanggliding. If these activities are part of the holiday, then you should include coverage of them on the video, or the record will be incomplete.

Some of these sports present difficulties. For a start, many of them take place near seawater, which has a habit of getting on equipment, with the risk of corrosion. You must take extra care. Alternatively splashproof housings are available for most camcorders at a price. A plastic bag can provide makeshift protection against light splashes.

When recording windsurfing, you will probably have to shoot at the telephoto limit of the zoom. Try a few practice shots to see how this will look in the frame. You may have to instruct the windsurfer to keep within certain limits if you wish to get close-up coverage – one windsurfer on the horizon looks much like any other and won't hold audience interest for very long.

Snorkelling is altogether more problematic, since all you can show is the snorkeller getting equipped and going out to sea. It may be possible to rent a special waterproof housing designed for recording underwater – it could be worth asking around if snorkelling is a major activity in the area. Alternatively, use a waterproof stills camera and transfer the stills onto video later.

1: Water skiing is a popular and spectacular holiday activity. It is also one for which it is relatively easy to get good coverage. Shooting from the power boat, you can get good close-up shots of the skier and the sound track will carry the noise of the boat. Beware of spray, though, and protect the camcorder with a plastic covering.

2: Poolside shots of members of the family enjoying a swim are easiest of all to capture. Get close-ups and the overall poolside scene.

3: Windsurfing provides dramatic and colourful shots, and is always worth including in a holiday video. This shot shows the windsurfer preparing to go for it.

4: A Bedouin horse race outside Marrakesh in Morocco. Treat it as you would any other race and take up a position that gives a full view of the action.

5: Out on the ski slopes you can get some impressive material. Skiing is a fast sport, so either take up a position and stick to it as the skiers come past, or pan an individual skier.

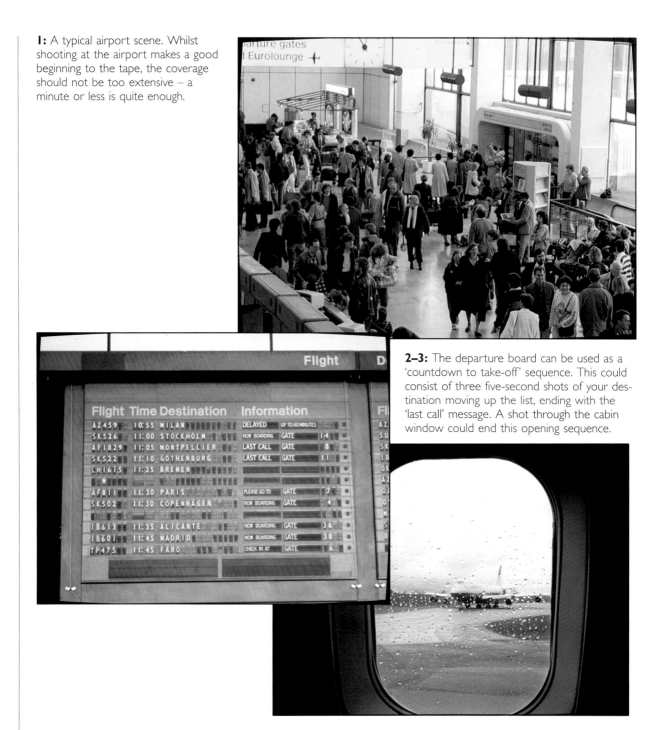

1: A typical airport scene. Whilst shooting at the airport makes a good beginning to the tape, the coverage should not be too extensive – a minute or less is quite enough.

2–3: The departure board can be used as a 'countdown to take-off' sequence. This could consist of three five-second shots of your destination moving up the list, ending with the 'last call' message. A shot through the cabin window could end this opening sequence.

Opening Shots

Journalists know that the opening sentences of an article are crucial. They must immediately catch the reader's attention, convey the story's essence, and compel him or her to read on. The principle applies equally well to making videos, for the opening shots must similarly 'hook' the viewer. But how do you decide on the most effective opening sequence?

When making a holiday video, an obvious opening sequence is of the family's frantic, last-minute attempts to finish packing. This effectively conveys a sense of anticipation, of the informal nature of the holiday, and introduces the members of the family to the viewer. However, unless the scene is particularly comic it could easily flop, becoming an uninteresting low-key record of a tedious chore. Consequently something far more dramatic is required to grip the viewer and set the scene.

An airport departure lounge has the necessary visual variety to make a lively introduction if filmed selectively. This particular scenario begins with a departure board's list of destinations, before zooming in on the right flight. Then comes

4: Arrival at the villa. Obviously to get this shot you (or an accomplice) will have to jump out of the car before the rest of the family to take up position. Framing the shot in the doorway emphasizes the fact of arrival.

5: A sequence on the beach the next day makes a good contrast to earlier airport scenes, indicating that you have well and truly arrived. If you choose this option, emphasize the contrast by making the sequence noisy and vibrant, shooting from close-up to capture the excitement on the children's faces.

6: If you are lucky enough to find a beach as deserted as this, make use of it. A sequence of the family walking along will convey a sense of relaxation and tranquillity.

further coverage of the passengers assembling as they wait to board the plane – but keep each shot very short as these pre-holiday sequences can drag on too long when replayed on screen.

This opening sequence could then cut to the arrival, but in so doing would miss out on interesting shots of *a* (not your!) plane's take-off, and the plane's interior. However, do check with the airline before filming because, whilst you will be allowed to take the camcorder on board as hand luggage, few airline companies permit inflight filming. The camcorder's electrical signals could dangerously interfere with the plane's highly sophisticated electronics.

Once you have indicated that you're up and away, conclude this opening sequence with scenes of your arrival. These could consist of signs in a foreign language, a scene giving a visible sense of 'having made it' as you unload your cases at the hotel, or a family's first moments on the beach.

1: The sequences establishing the villa are relatively straightforward. They were taken early in the morning when there was deep shadow and little glare. The bright colour of the flowers in the foreground helps to balance the image. The shot continues with the family emerging from the villa to inspect the garden.

2–3: The luxuriant vegetation around the villa made a great impression on arrival. Close-up shots of the plants, showing the rich range of green, bright red and purple flowers, are of much greater interest than simply showing the garden in long-shot. The sequences were shot from a crouching position, which is much more effective and natural than pointing the camera downwards.

Establishers and Links

Shots of the location which show the viewer where the action is taking place are known as *establishing shots*, or establishers. They usually come at the very beginning of a sequence, although you may choose to start with a teasing shot – by homing in on a particular feature of the scene, before pulling back slowly with the zoom to reveal the context and location of the video.

The action you are recording will usually dictate the nature of the establisher. In the holiday video the family's villa was obviously an important location, being the starting point of all their excursions. Several establishers of this location were therefore shot, including the villa itself, various aspects of the garden, and the view from the garden out to sea.

Whenever possible try to include action in an establisher, even if it's only of a major character setting off on an outing. Preferably, such establishers should be in long-shot so that the figure does not dominate the scene. Hold the shot just long enough for the audience to absorb the information, but no more because, as there is no real action, they will start to lose interest.

4–5: These two shots are from a brief exploration of the surrounding area soon after the family arrived at the villa. In video terms, they are really no more than picture postcards. People are usually so impressed by their new surroundings on arriving in a new country that there is a dangerous temptation to linger for too long on such scenes.

Linking shots

With an informal video, such as one of a holiday, you have much greater freedom to include additional material. Since you are not really concerned with telling a highly structured, formal story (beyond recording what you did and what you saw), sequences do not necessarily have to build on preceding images. So, between a sequence of, say, the villa and its surroundings, and one of a day on the beach, you can shoot short links of anything that might be of interest, such as highly attractive views, local characters, or colourful street scenes or market traders selling their wares.

When shooting other kinds of video, perhaps a drama or documentary, you will find link material equally valuable, particularly if you are going to edit your tape. In most cases, the inclusion of links between main sequences implies the passing of time. Of course, the links should have some relevance to the story being told – audiences are easily distracted and puzzled if the camera lingers on something for no purpose at all.

Pace and Balance

Pace and balance in video work are hard to define precisely. They imply a pleasing flow of images, with no sequence being unduly longer than any other. Pace and balance are also achieved by contrasting sequences – perhaps by following an introspective moment with frenetic activity – and by gradually increasing the tempo. But there are no hard and fast rules for achieving this aim. You have to develop a feeling for it, as when getting the balance 'right' in composing a single shot.

As you are filming, remember this important need for pace and balance (it helps if you look at the scene in the viewfinder as if it were unfolding on a television screen).

Obviously, if you are going to edit the tape, you will be able to fine-tune the pace of your sequences at this later stage. But even if you are limited to in-camera editing, you can still achieve balance by thinking about the length and content of your sequences beforehand. (A useful tip is to write down the intended duration of each sequence to be covered.)

Let's consider the example of a day's outing to a nearby town. The coverage will include scenes of the family at the local market, a sequence on the beach, the afternoon meal, and places of local interest. A shooting plan would allocate three minutes to the market, five to the beach, and a minute each to the meal and local scenes.

Don't forget that there must be a sense of pace and balance *within* each individual sequence, as well as *between* sequences.

Also, avoid the temptation to instil pace into sequences by changes of camera angle and by moving from long-shot to close-up and vice versa, particularly if the action you are recording is relatively commonplace. As has already been stressed, too much intrusive camera action is distracting for the viewer.

And finally, ensure that within sequences shots are of equal pace. So, for instance, you should never cut from a fast long-shot pan of a scene to a slow pan of an individual walking in close-up: the difference in pace will merely confuse the viewer.

1–3: The market sequence simply, but very effectively. follows the family as they soak up the atmosphere. A quiet·word between father and daughter brings a moment of intimacy.

4–6: Separate shots of interesting displays, and the family reactions to them, help to create a change of pace within the sequence. So the appreciation of fine lacework contrasts with buying a beach ball or children's clothes.

7–8: Although the film of the family on the beach shows them highly relaxed, it doesn't mean you can stop thinking about your techniques. The shots of the young child engrossed in playing on the sand give a pleasing change of pace from the faster action of the football game.

129

1–2: This sequence of a child waking up has a slow, gentle pace. It will act as a useful punctuation between some of the more lively, dynamic scenes of the holiday video.

3: The charm of the subject and the simplicity of the setting means that the technique has also been kept simple. A slight movement of the camera to ensure the child is kept within the frame as she emerges from the bed-clothes is all that is needed.

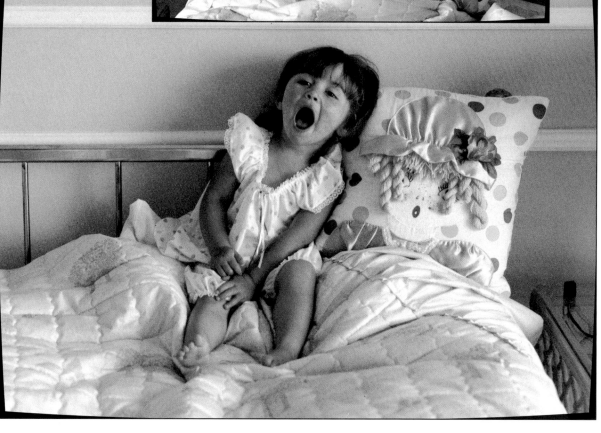

1–2: This fast-paced sequence is typical of many holiday beach scenes. The rapid movement of the footballers was followed with a fast pan in long-shot.

3: A close-up like this following a fast pan will work if the subject is still moving. It adds to the sense of action – but you will have to have good reactions to capture such a shot successfully.

1: The light by the sea can be quite dazzling and contrast can therefore be greater than the camcorder can cope with. The highlight on the rock background just avoids an ugly 'burn out'.

2: This shot is evenly lit and is less likely to cause problems. A polarizing filter could have been used here to cut out all surface reflections and show the clear depths of the water.

3: Strong backlighting should be avoided even if you have a backlight button to apply some correction. This shot is typical of the muddy colours and loss of detail of backlit shots.

Sun, Sea and Sky

The beach in sunny weather can be an ideal place to shoot video, but taking your camcorder on to unfamiliar ground has its potential pitfalls.

The coastal environment can be hazardous to video gear. Avoid loading your tape cassettes into the camcorder in windy conditions as gritty dust, sand and salt sea-spray can wreak havoc with the video heads. Keep the camcorder lens covered except when it is actually being used and protect it with a screw-on plain glass filter – an ultraviolet or skylight filter will do fine.

Don't leave the camcorder lying about in the hot sun and be sure not to get it wet – so keep it clear of the sea and don't use it in the rain, either. Some camcorders can be fully waterproofed for underwater use by placing them in a special housing – these are more expensive the deeper they allow you to take the camera beneath the water's surface. Special rain hoods can also provide some protection.

Be sure you have sufficient cassettes to see you through the holiday – additional tapes may not be readily available at the location.

Power supply

Another important point to remember is that you will need to be able to recharge your camcorder batteries as you go. You will therefore need the availability of a mains power supply to plug your battery charger into. When you are travelling abroad, remember that different countries use different types of mains plugs as well as varying voltages. Take the relevant adaptor. Plugging the camcorder into your car's lighter socket, with an accessory lead called a battery eliminator, is another useful tip for saving battery power on a trip.

4: The colour and appearance of subjects depends to a large extent on the direction and 'colour temperature' of the light. This was shot with full sun behind the camcorder user and therefore the colours are fully saturated and vivid.

5: The same scene was taken at a different time of day. The conditions are hazy with the sun shining from the top right-hand corner of the frame. The result of this backlit shot is muted colours and emphasis on the shape of the shoreline.

6: A sunny action shot which is three-quarters sidelit to throw the subjects into relief. The only photographic hazard is the sea spray, which must not be allowed to get onto the camcorder!

Recording Wildlife

Natural history can become an absorbing interest, and can provide fascinating video material. To make a video recording of wildlife requires great patience. You must investigate all aspects of your subject's behaviour – how the animal feeds, where it sleeps, when it mates, and how it reacts to the presence of man. You may need to spend weeks observing the animal, noting down its every move.

Once the animal's habits are known, you will be in a position to set up a hide and begin recording. A bait of water or food can be used to persuade it to come out into the open. Count on a lengthy stay and take with you food, drink and binoculars.

Ideally, you should work with a long lens. The longest focal length on a typical 12x zoom camcorder is equivalent to having a 500mm on a 35mm-format stills camera. This produces excellent magnification for most wildlife. If this doesn't get you close enough, then you will have to use a telephoto adaptor to extend your lens power. You will also need a heavy tripod, since with this range of magnification the slightest tremor can seem like an earthquake on screen.

To record sound as well as image, you will need an extension microphone, positioned in a concealed place close to where you believe the animal will appear. A superdirectional mic with a pick-up zone of about 90 degrees will produce the best results.

Never disturb an animal's natural habitat. This means not pulling down vegetation in order to get a clear view. This is particularly important with nesting birds – even if the bird itself is not disturbed, any change in the vegetation will give away the presence of the nest to predators.

Of course, it is not necessary to trek into the wilderness to record wildlife. The bird table in the garden is a good place to start. Safari parks and open zoos are also ideal. Here, you will have to shoot from a car – never be tempted to get out to obtain a better shot. Brace the camcorder against the window frame, preferably using a small clamp. Keep the engine running and have the car pointing towards an escape route in case large animals show signs of resenting your intrusion!

2: This howler monkey could easily be in its natural habitat in the Amazonian rain forest. In fact it was shot in an open zoo. With a long zoom setting, it was possible to record the monkeys' behaviour in detail, including close-ups of facial expressions and gestures between members of the group.

3: The problem with animals in some zoos is that they appear inactive. In fact, many animals in the wild spend their time dozing between meals. This big cat was recorded at a zoo in which the animals were kept in large enclosures.

4: Animals in cages or behind bars prove a problem. Use the limited depth of field of the telephoto lens to blur out the bars in the foreground. Get as close to the bars as possible, and use a fast shutter speed so that the camera selects a wide aperture. Remember also to use manual focusing.

1 (left): A telephoto adaptor is ideal for recording animals perching in tall trees so that you get that extra bit of zoom power.

5: A magnificent jaguar on the prowl. When recording animals in zoos, check out feeding times beforehand. Animals usually get restless as feeding time approaches and the sight of a big cat tearing into a chunk of meat provides exciting coverage.

The Macro Lens

On many camcorders, the zoom lens also offers a macro option – a lens setting that allows you to record subjects that are very close to the lens at high magnifications. Usually, this mode is obtained by adjusting the lens to the widest setting. The camera may then automatically focus down to just a few millimetres from the lens, or you may have to use a manual macro focusing control.

The setting works by rearranging the lens elements so that those at the rear are moved forward, altering the light path to give a high degree of magnification. In effect, the lens arrangement inside the zoom becomes equivalent to that used in a microscope. The most obvious use for the macro setting is for recording small objects such as plants and insects, in close-up. At the macro setting, depth of field is very shallow, particularly when a wide lens aperture has been set by the automatic exposure system. This means that you will require a high level of ambient light when recording, and additional lighting is advisable.

The shallow depth of field, and the magnification of the image obtained, means that it is best to take macro shots with a tripod. This places limits on field work. You will obtain better results if the environment is controlled – a short documentary sequence on insect behaviour, for example, could be made by placing the insects inside a specially built glass-sided container.

1: Part of a sequence in an English meadow, this macro shot provides a welcome break from a succession of long-shots that included little interesting detail.

2: This is an even closer shot of the inside of one of the flowers. The specimen had to be screened from the wind to prevent movement because of the shallow depth of field.

3: A glass tank, good lighting, and a tripod-mounted camera were essential for this shot of butterflies mating. A black felt backdrop behind the tank ensures that the butterflies stand out clearly. Patience is as important as the right technique when tackling this type of subject.

4: Caterpillars are excellent subjects — there is plenty of movement, but it is mostly in one plane, so depth of field is not a problem.

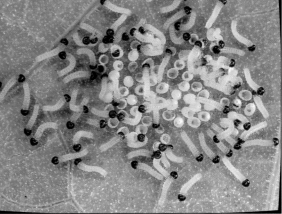

5: When recording insects, be prepared for short-shots, before the subject takes flight — so you need to be prepared, and act quickly. The problem with this shot of a bee is that we can't get all of its body in focus at the same time due to the very shallow depth of field.

137

1: The fountains and crowds outside St Peter's, Rome, give the scene a sense of movement that the building itself lacks.

Architecture

Buildings are one of the most common subjects that you will encounter on holiday. They are often among the most interesting features of a foreign town, and you will want to film them to give a faithful impression of your visit. But because buildings do not move they are difficult to video. It can also be hard to get far enough away from a building to include all of it in the frame. One solution is to record the life around the building – the throngs of people in an Italian square or the guards outside a royal palace. This will help convey the atmosphere of the place but will not give a sense of the architectural details that make the building what it is. To do this you will need to pan slowly across the structure, or shoot a series of close-ups highlighting the most telling details. You should also look for unusual camera positions, to avoid the obvious views of your subject.

Another interesting possibility is to use the building as a vantage point, and film the view as well as the building itself. Church spires and domes, castle towers, and skyscrapers all lend themselves to this approach. It will not only give you a new angle on the building's setting, but may also offer a good way of recording other places you have already visited on your holiday – in fact you will be amazed at what you can see!

2–3: Inside the church, the dome is the most imposing architectural feature. These shots are taken from a sequence in which the camera began by recording details.

4: The camera has pulled back to show the whole of the dome.

5: After a sequence showing the dome, a shot looking down from the gallery helps to put the dome in context. It also gives a wide enough angle of view to take in parts of the church that would otherwise be difficult to record.

Closing a Sequence

It is an accepted rule that before beginning a shot you should know how it is going to end. For example, if you are planning a slow pan of a beach scene you should rehearse it to ensure that the shot ends on an interesting or attractive feature. In addition, the shot which closes a sequence should be static, so preparing the audience for the change to a new image at the commencement of the next sequence. In effect, the static frame at the close acts as a visual full stop.

There are a number of accepted, if rather clichéd, devices for concluding a sequence. These can be determined either by the action, or the camera. For example, in a drama, a typical concluding shot to a sequence might well include someone walking slowly out of shot, away from the camera. Alternatively, the figure might leave a room, with the camera briefly resting on the closed door. While such shots are often highly appropriate, you may prefer to veer away from the obvious, if instantly recognizable end, to more original conclusions.

Another type of closing shot can be created in-camera, either via concluding camera movement, or by adjusting the focus or, in certain situations, the exposure. The most obvious camera movement for a closing shot is the slow pan coming to rest on either a significant detail, or an image of the location seen in long shot. In the vacation video, a shot was taken of the harbour towards evening, panning round and then coming to rest on the deserted beach. Both camera movement and content indicate the end of the sequence.

Other techniques involve throwing the scene out of focus at the end of the shot. If the next sequence begins out of focus too, the audience will take this as an indication that time has passed, having been trained to interpret such conventions by television and film makers. In fact, the more of these conventions you use the more sophisticated your videos will appear, and the more information you will be able to convey to viewers in a short time span. Another effect involves gradually closing down the aperture to darken the scene.

1–3: For a sequence of a barbecue, when we have shot the preparations of the fire and the party eating, we could end with a shot of candles gradually going out of focus.

4–5: These shots illustrate a typical end to a sequence. The bathers are running out of the sea and out of shot. Make sure that initially there is enough lead space, and that the subjects cross the screen on the diagonal. The final shot rests on the beach itself with the yacht in the distance.

6: This scene contains the elements required to end a sequence. The shot is taken from a position of deep shade into strong sunlight. The shot ends with the door closing and the screen darkening almost to black.

141

Project Notebook

HOLIDAYS

A family holiday video is not going to be the next *Citizen Kane*. But it does offer an opportunity to shoot in a new, and often interesting, location, and to get shots of your family and friends having a good time. The intention should be to convey a relaxed, entertaining atmosphere, and if you adopt that approach when you shoot, then you are ten times more likely to convey that impression to the viewer. If you do, then you've made a good video.

■ Check the relevant customs regulations concerning the import and export of equipment.

■ Pack your equipment carefully. Have you got enough tape and batteries? Do you need special filters? Do you have a travel plug adaptor?

■ What is the TV standard used in the country of your destination, and is it compatible with your equipment?

■ Every picture tells a story. A little forward planning should enable you to incorporate a beginning, a middle and an end to your holiday video, thus greatly increasing the audience-interest factor.

■ You can't video yourself. Obvious, yes, but this means that if you want shots of the family arriving at the hotel or villa, you'll have to get someone else to operate the camcorder, or arrive earlier yourself, and 'fake' it.

■ Don't contrive too many sequences – you're on holiday as well!

■ Remember, intense sunlight, sand and seawater are not best friends to the video camera's sensitive electronics.

■ In some countries, locals do not take lightly to having a camcorder pointed at them. Always be polite and ask permission before shooting.

Developing a Story

The home video maker is immediately faced by two decisions –
What's my story? and How am I going to treat it? For instance, are
you going for a relatively straightforward approach, perhaps revealing how events unfold over the course of a day, or will you opt for
a more sophisticated line? This might involve creating a cast of up
to five characters, revealing how their relationships develop.

Once such general considerations have been tackled, you must
set about more specific problems. In the following video project we
reveal how to film a community of nuns. As you'll see, such a
potentially general subject throws up a huge number of possibilities, continuously forcing you to redefine your aims until you have
a specific storyline and viewpoint. Without it the film will lack
focus and coherence, and you will stand little chance of holding
your audience's attention.

First Approaches

Good shots of buildings are in some ways more difficult to obtain than those of people. People, after all, are usually doing something, which in itself creates interest. With buildings, movement is implied by the camerawork alone. So the camcorder must explore a building as would the human eye.

The first sequence in the video establishes the location for the action. There are a number of ways of doing this. Most approaches would begin with a long-shot and then move in for more detail. Any detail that is to be highlighted should be significant – it could be a signboard revealing the location or the landscape if it is going to have a significant effect on the action.

Such sequences are necessarily static: movement comes from changing the camera position and the focal length of the zoom lens – or by panning or tilting the camera.

Another option is a moving shot, taken either on foot or from a car. Although you will undoubtedly get camera shake, this will also provide additional drama. The viewer will interpret this movement as an arrival, and from then on will identify with the camera's 'eye' as it surveys the convent.

1–3: A pan shot of the impressive exterior of the convent both establishes the location and indicates a feeling of serenity and history.

4–6: The next step is to consider shots taken from a position mid-way along the driveway to the convent. This approach adds to the sense of arrival, but the car parked outside the convent distracts attention. If in a subsequent sequence the car has disappeared, the viewers will wonder whether this has any significance.

7: Shooting the scene from an unusual angle is another way of giving visual impact – such as with the high-angle shot from the the roof pictured on the right. By beginning the sequence with a close-up detail that doesn't indicate the nature of the whole, followed by a zoom out from the subject which is then fully revealed, the audience will experience first puzzlement and then recognition. However, although such a technique is useful it wasn't considered for the video of the convent – it seemed ill-suited to the pace of convent life.

8–9: It is also important to maintain a coherent sense of geography within the sequences so that the viewer knows where something is happening. The important locations here are the chapel, the courtyard and the dining room. Try to keep the locations to a minimum, instead of endlessly shifting from one place to another. You don't have to show everything to convey the sense of full coverage.

10: From the outside the convent could be mistaken for a stately home, or even a private school. In fact, the house became a convent only recently and the documentary tells the story of its past alongside the contemporary life of the nuns. This shot is of an effigy on a tomb in the chapel where the nuns worship several times every day and it makes a good link between the past and the present households.

Planning the Structure

The first question to resolve is how to plan your approach to your subject. Research will have already helped you fill out your ideas, and may have suggested alternative treatments. Now, as you will see in this chapter's example of a video featuring a convent, a number of basic story lines immediately suggest themselves.

In the first, you could concentrate on the life of the whole community over a 24-hour period. It would begin with early morning prayers, examine the different tasks that have to be undertaken during the day, and conclude with the sisters assembling in the evening to have dinner and celebrate their faith.

An alternative approach would concentrate on personalities: What is the Mother Superior's role? How is life viewed by a novice? But although the idea is valid, conversation with the sisters quickly revealed that they did not see their community in terms of a hierarchy. For them, each member had equally valued contributions to make. Consequently a treatment based on personalities

should reflect this view that the community has of itself. Another possible approach would show the sisters engaged in vital social work, helping teenagers from deprived backgrounds to overcome their problems. Whichever approach you choose, try to keep to it consistently through the video.

By clarifying your intent in this way, you can establish the structure of the video in greater detail. And once you have established an objective you must then decide how best to realize your aims. The three sequences, shown in the pictures below, illustrate three different story ideas, revealing how each might affect the way you approach the video as a whole.

1–12: When planning a video of this type, work out beforehand the range of different shots it could contain. They will include everything from close-ups to long-shots, and from solemn scenes to witty ones. Notice that you can immediately start looking for cutaways and interesting angles to add visual variety to your video.

Storyboard and Script

Having decided on the basic theme you want to get across, the next stage is to draw up a synopsis and then a storyboard – a detailed plan of what you intend to shoot. In professional work the storyboard is the preliminary to a shooting script, giving details of each shot, including its subject matter, the camera angle, type of shot and duration. (It is not always practical to go into this much detail when working on one's own.) The sequences you include in the storyboard should have been very clearly worked out. A shortened script, in which you detail points that have occurred to you while planning the storyboard, will prove to be invaluable on the day on the shoot.

1: A long-shot of the convent opens the video and establishes where the action is taking place. The building is so impressive that it forms a major part of the story. The sequence was taken from a tripod and contains a slow, controlled zoom, which was rehearsed first.

2: The storyboard here contains 12 main areas, representing key sequences that will constitute the complete video. This gives us a rough idea of the video so that we can visualize the pace, and should allow us to spot mistakes in continuity, items that are missing from the story or shots that might look better elsewhere in the video. These can be rough representations – so it doesn't matter if you can't draw very well. Later you can write a list of detailed notes about shots you hope to get in the shooting script.

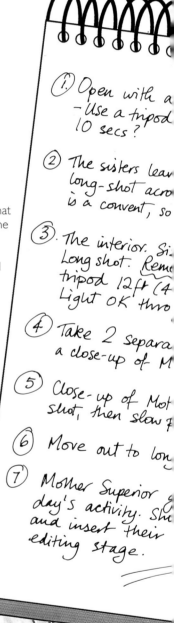

① Open with a
 – Use a tripod
10 secs?

② The sisters leav
long-shot acro
is a convent, so

③ The interior. Si
Long shot. Reme
tripod 12 ft (4
Light OK thro

④ Take 2 separa
a close-up of M

⑤ Close-up of Mot
shot, then slow p

⑥ Move out to lon

⑦ Mother Superior
day's activity. Sh
and insert their
editing stage.

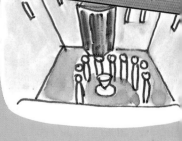

Below: The shooting script can be as detailed as you like. Putting the information into two columns is a good idea. Give a brief description of the shot on the left-hand side and any special notes on the right.

3: Sequences showing the nuns relaxing helped to pace the video between the more significant set pieces, such as prayers, worship and meals. The sisters were consulted beforehand, so they were not startled out of their repose by the unexpected presence of a cameraman. Forewarned, they were able to appear quite 'natural'.

4: Worship was a very important part of the life of the community, and became a major element in the story. Although their services were simple and intimate, it was not difficult to obtain good coverage without being too intrusive.

5: Several closing sequences immediately suggested themselves. The original decision to conclude the video with a shot of the convent building was rejected in favour of the nuns and lay members at their evening meal. Since most camcorders will record well even in moderately bright candlelight, this shouldn't be a problem.

t of the main front.
n. Poss duration

door. Use with a
Establish building
ns in context.

ning prayer.
balance. Set
KEEP QUIET.
ow ??

long-shot and
rior.

r. Hold the
er sisters.

ld.

t talk on
separately
at

Introducing the Characters

So far, the first sequence in the video has answered the question 'Where?' The next question is 'Who?' In other words, the video must establish the characters on whom we are going to focus. If you watch television programmes closely, you'll notice that in most drama and documentary the number of major characters is limited to perhaps four or five. Any more and the plot could easily get out of hand, with audiences failing to identify with anyone. So while other people may appear, the story and our attention concentrates on these figures alone.

Although the community of nuns is small enough for everyone to appear, a number of individuals stand out. A sequence such as that of the nuns at prayer allows the camera to rest on the faces of all those taking part, giving viewers adequate time to remember and note the full 'cast'. But because of her role at prayer, it's quite clear that the Mother Superior is a leading character.

Other characters to appear are the lay members who share the sisters' everyday tasks. They are gradually introduced working in the kitchen or the garden, so ensuring that not too many characters are introduced simultaneously. Subsequent coverage of the sisters and lay members dining and talking together revealed how the community is integrated together.

One point that applies to this project, and to video work in general, is avoiding close-ups in which the subject is looking straight at the camera (easier said than done). It's far better to film people at work or tackling a job, so conveying something about them and not about their self-consciousness in front of the camera.

Another useful tip when filming groups of people is to follow eyelines as the camera moves from one subject to another. It not only looks more natural, but also helps to establish a relationship between the characters.

1–9: Whilst carrying out your research you will have decided which characters you wish to feature. Of necessity some will be more prominent, depending on their personalities and the story you have chosen. Since no video can tell the whole story, this is neither wrong nor misleading. From the pictures here it is easy to see who are the main characters – as they feature prominently in close-ups. Wider shots show their relationships with others who have been given less screen time.

Holding the Viewer

A video consists of a series of sequences which combine to tell a story. Each individual sequence should have a coherent structure with a beginning, middle and end. Without it your viewers will quickly become lost.

Sequences should begin by concentrating on the main subject of the shot. This is usually best done by having the subject in long-shot – close-ups introduce the subject too suddenly. The sequences in the convent video mainly show the sisters at work, in discussion or with guests. While they are talking the film concentrates on and highlights their various relationships. Two-shots and slow pans from face to face, following the eye-line to record the expressions of the participants, concentrate the viewers' interest on the subject. The camera moves should therefore be motivated by what is happening in the scene – unnecessary changes of angle will reveal little about the characters' personalities and irritate the audience.

When you are filming people at work, viewers will want to see exactly what is going on. When shooting in a kitchen, for instance, you should let the camera rest on the ingredients, and show the pots and pans, and cooking facilities. Filming the cook at work, for instance, over-the-shoulder shots provide a clear view of a meal being prepared. Another interesting technique is to include the occasional close-up of the main subject's hands, showing precisely how she is tackling that recipe.

The end of a sequence should be as logical and assured as the beginning. By thinking about the close of a shot before you commence filming you can avoid poor sequences that badly fall away, so undermining what's gone before. For example, in a kitchen sequence, the shot can close with the food being imaginatively arranged on serving dishes, signalling the end of the preparation and providing a lead into the meal itself. In other instances your 'characters' can be briefed to perform a 'closing' action, such as shutting a book or leaving a room, anything that will be interpreted by the viewer as an ending.

I–5: This sequence shows an amusing conversation between two of the sisters. It begins as a long-shot showing them walking towards the camera. They stop, and the camera zooms in very slightly closer. The conversation is recorded in a mid-shot containing both participants.

3: To get in closer still, the camera gradually arcs round to frame the nuns against the plain background of the hedge. This concentrates our attention on the conversation, so we are not distracted by anything that might happen in the distance.

4: The sister obviously had some important news to tell, and as she is the principal speaker the audience's attention will be most drawn to her. The actual news was about a minor catastrophe that occurred in the kitchen earlier in the day.

5: In this sequence, changes in shot were kept to a minimum. The interest for the audience is in what is occurring in front of the camera. Although a close-up on the sister is tempting, it would deprive the audience of seeing the second sister's reaction to the news.

1: Another sequence in the documentary on life in the convent concentrated on one of the sisters who was an accomplished player of the lyre. The sequence opened with the sister shown in long-shot sitting in the convent courtyard, an attractive setting chosen earlier in the day.

2: To continue the sequence, the camera moved to a position slightly behind the sister's left shoulder. This avoided her being shown head-on, which would have been a rather unnatural-looking shot if held too long.

3: Moving in the camera closer still, the shot continued by going into a close-up of the lyre and the sister's fingers on the strings. It is this sort of detail that the audience is interested in and the shot was held for about thirty seconds, before the sequence ended with a long-shot as the music came to an end.

4: Don't forget that the interference caused by the camera operator can become part of the story. This sequence is intended to capture the sister engrossed in her paperwork, but she soon finds she cannot keep up the pretence.

5: One of the unspoken conventions of many television documentaries is the pretence that the camera isn't really there. In reality, most people respond to its presence and find it difficult to pretend otherwise. The sister was unable to resist glancing upwards towards the camera. This could be cut out at the editing stage.

6: The sister's reaction to the presence of the camera, however, became itself part of the story related in the sequence. In fact, by responding to the intrusion in the way she does, she reveals her gentle sense of humour and adds great charm to this simple sequence.

Changes of Pace

An important way to hold audience attention involves varying the pace between different sequences. Pace is partly a matter of timing the length of each sequence, and is partly conveyed by what is happening on the screen.

The early sequences of the video of the community are slow and gentle, showing the building and introducing the nuns at prayer. The closing sequences were planned to convey a similar mood. But if the whole video were to be shot in this way, the effect would become monotonous. Consequently it was planned to increase the tempo during the middle stages, for which a relatively lively action sequence was required. It was decided that the sisters' recreation period in the late afternoon would fill this gap, while reinforcing the sense of informality in the community.

The sisters were asked if they would play a game of football! They readily agreed, since they sometimes played with groups of youngsters who visit the convent. An informal series of shots of the sisters at play, shot handheld, in both close-up and long-shot, provides the change in pace required. That some of the shots are shaky, and sometimes a little out of focus, is no disadvantage and will make the sequence seem more natural.

Most video projects will contain an opportunity for similar sequences. For example, in a video portrait of a local school, the frantic activity in the playground can be contrasted with the quiet periods of study. If you were shooting life in a small town, the activity in the market could be contrasted with the peace and quiet in a local park or in the surrounding rural landscape. Try to think of as many opportunities as possible for varying pace when you plan your video.

1: Start of the game: the sisters come out to play football. The sequence requires no formal treatment, and begins with the sisters approaching the camera.

2: By shooting with a handheld camera in amongst the game itself, a sense of excitement and involvement is immediately conveyed to the viewers.

3: The sisters soon lose their self-consciousness as the game progresses. Shots of the ball coming straight towards the camera are always effective in such sequences.

4: In effect these shots show the point-of-view of one of the players. Taken from an onlooker's viewpoint, the shots would have been too static for the required change of pace.

5–7: These shots are from a sequence in the kitchen. They were shot in a more formal way, to convey a sense of people getting on with their work. From the point of view of pacing the video, their effect is, in fact, to increase the tempo from an earlier, more contemplative scene.

Left: This diagram gives some idea of the pacing of the video. The main sequences are outlined in red, and the shorter 'interludes' in blue. The viewer will still follow the narrative of the tape, since the narrative sequences predominate. The interludes are discrete sequences in themselves, giving extra description, rather than adding to the story itself.

Interludes

Most projects can be conceived in terms of major sequences. They can be interspersed with shorter pieces revealing interesting details and asides, adding more visual variety. Since the viewer's interest in the story being told is satisfied by the overall structure of the tape, these 'interludes' can be of almost anything relevant to the subject. Of course, the more visually interesting these images are, the better.

The photographs on this page show some of the types of shots available. The image of the sister in the mirror, taken in the great hall, is a good example. The mirror frame itself has a rich texture, and the slight distortion adds interest. Reflection shots are available in many situations and it's worth thinking about such possibilities beforehand. However, do ensure that there is no chance of your reflection being caught in the mirror. On the other hand, there may be some instances where you could make a feature of this. In such instances close in on the reflection so that it is clear this is a deliberate technique.

Interesting architectural details are also well worth including. The convent has many such features, but if shown as a continuous sequence they might well fail to hold the interest of some viewers. However, if used as an interlude they can even enliven the film.

Another technique for adding interest involved a lay member of the community reading from an appropriate text in the Bible, while the camera recorded the stained glass and statue in the chapel. This works well, providing a contrast on the sound track too. It also provides a good concluding point to the shot, with the reader coming to the end of the text and closing the book.

1–2: The main point of this additional coverage is to provide visual variety, and a greater visual texture to the video. Shots of the sisters at their needlework (**1**), or in the hall (**2**), convey the everyday life in the community, and give a sense of time passing.

3–4: Other shots of such details as spring flowers in a vase **(3)**, and a close-up of the stained glass **(4)**, could be used as cutaways when the tape is edited. Of course, with editing in mind, it is better to shoot too much material than too little. What you don't want can always be left out later.

5: The lay reader provides an interesting and appropriate soundtrack by reading from the Bible while the camera surveys the chapel. The shot was set up next to the carved head for added visual interest. Oddly enough, there is a distinct resemblance.

Documentary Checklist

Subject ....

VENUE RECONNAISSANCE

Place	Date	Time	Transport	Accommodation
_____	_____	_____	_____	_____
_____	_____	_____	_____	_____
_____	_____	_____	_____	_____

SHOOTING PLAN

INTRODUCTION

Place	Date	Time	Details of Coverage
_____	_____	_____	_____
_____	_____	_____	_____
_____	_____	_____	_____
_____	_____	_____	_____

MAIN THEMES

Place	Date	Time	Details of Coverage
_____	_____	_____	_____
_____	_____	_____	_____
_____	_____	_____	_____
_____	_____	_____	_____

CUTAWAYS

Place	Date	Time	Details of Coverage
_____	_____	_____	_____
_____	_____	_____	_____
_____	_____	_____	_____
_____	_____	_____	_____
_____	_____	_____	_____
_____	_____	_____	_____

ALTERNATIVES
Place | Date | Time | Details of Coverage

_____ | _____ | _____ | _____

_____ | _____ | _____ | _____

_____ | _____ | _____ | _____

_____ | _____ | _____ | _____

CLOSING SEQUENCES
Place | Date | Time | Details of Coverage

_____ | _____ | _____ | _____

_____ | _____ | _____ | _____

_____ | _____ | _____ | _____

_____ | _____ | _____ | _____

CONTACTS

Name | Address | Telephone Number

_____ | _____ | _____

_____ | _____ | _____

_____ | _____ | _____

_____ | _____ | _____

_____ | _____ | _____

_____ | _____ | _____

_____ | _____ | _____

_____ | _____ | _____

_____ | _____ | _____

EQUIPMENT REQUIREMENTS

☐ CAMCORDER AND ACCESSORIES . . . .

☐ BATTERIES . . . .

☐ LIGHTING . . . .

☐ TAPES . . . .

The Final Sequences

The final sequences should bring the video to a satisfying and appropriate conclusion. In a drama, the final sequence might be designed to shock the viewer and leave a lasting impression in the mind.

In a documentary exploring a controversial issue, the piece could end with a question, prompting further thought. With most such topics the issues are not black and white, and however thorough your video has been there is always more room for debate. Of course, the way you hope the viewer will answer this final question will be swayed by at least some of the arguments that you have brought forward.

The intention of this project was to convey the sense of peace and fellowship present in the community. There were two obvious choices for ending the tape: the sisters at evening prayer, or the community gathered together for the final meal of the day. Both would bring this 'life-in-a-day' approach to an appropriate end.

Remember that the closing sequence will be the last thing that the audience will see, and that this will likely be the thing that sticks in its mind. On this occasion, it was decided that the ending in the chapel was too obvious, and didn't show the sense of community that the makers were trying to highlight. The candlelit dinner with the lay members seemed a much better ending.

1–2: At the evening meal the sisters and various lay members gather together. They dine by candlelight, but while there is sufficient light to film, the image is dark, so there is a temptation to turn on additional lighting (**1**). But this tends to kill the atmosphere, so it was better to make do with the candlelight (**2**). As there are deep shadow areas in the shots, it seemed appropriate to bring the video to close with a gradual fade to black.

3: The alternative closing sequence – the sudden cut to the sisters at evening prayer – would have disturbed the pace of the video. Had this sequence been used it would have been introduced by shots of the sisters arriving at the chapel. This would have been pertinent since it confirmed the sense of a fellowship, while the exterior shots prepared the viewer for what was to follow.

4–6: The earlier sequence of the sisters at prayer was taken from quite close up and from shoulder height. For the final sequence a high-angle shot was used. This gives visual variety and a sense of distancing. A slow zoom out leaves the sisters at worship, and a slow tilt allows the camera to rest on the stained glass window. The camera movements have to be slow and smooth to convey a sense of peace.

Research

What you don't know, you can't shoot. Consequently the more exhaustively you research your subject, the more ideas you'll have when creating the storyline, and the greater the chances of including interesting, unusual sequences to flesh out the main plot.

You don't have to do lots of preparation before you leave; the best material is often only found once you have reached your location. The materials on this spread were acquired during a weekend trip to Paris. In addition to suggesting subjects for filming, the postcards, street plans and timetables can also be used to make an atmospheric introduction to the video – to be used as backgrounds for a title sequence or as still life shots on their own.

Thinking visually

Once you have chosen your subject areas, you must decide how best to film them. When shooting a scene that is relatively unfamiliar to your viewer, you should keep your techniques and innovative camera angles to a minimum. In other words, as director/camera operator you don't want your techniques to obstruct your audience's appreciation of the images. Viewers should be concentrating on the sequences and not how you are using the camera.

But with a familiar landmark, why not show it from a striking, unusual angle, enabling people to see it as if for the first time?

You could also consider making visual contrasts. So, a sequence of the Arc de Triomphe, with its famous classical outlines, might gain when followed by shots of the ultra-modernist Pompidou Centre. Or would the juxtaposition be too jarring for the gentle, romantic pace you want for the video?

Do also keep an eye out for detail – interesting shop fronts, window displays, and colourful posters could well merit a close-up. These are not only interesting in their own right, but will provide useful cutaways when it comes to editing.

In addition to such filming techniques there are other practicalities to note. There will be some areas or buildings where you cannot get permission to film. In others, filming will only be possible after you have obtained written approval. And in other instances, as when filming in a restaurant, it is only polite to gain the manager's permission first.

And finally, do check on opening – some buildings will not be open every day of the week, and others might close off-season. If you get them wrong, and are filming while on holiday, there may not be time to return for a second shoot.

SOURCES OF INFORMATION

The nature of a project will, to a certain extent, determine which are the most appropriate sources of information. If, for instance, you are making a video of farm life, the most profitable research would be a visit to the farm enabling you to witness exactly what goes on. Discussion with the farmer and the workers would establish further points of interest that you might decide to shoot. However, for most other video projects you will probably need to consult some of the following sources:

Libraries. Besides being sources of general information, libraries often have materials of specific local interest which might yield profitable ideas.

Tourist authorities. Tourist board brochures and guides are excellent for checking that you have not omitted any places of interest.

City authorities. Municipal authorities provide a similar service. Many have information offices which will readily inform you of local interests and problems.

Newspapers. The 'locals' are an excellent source of information, listing festivals, street markets and other attractions.

Specialist societies. Specialist and local societies are usually very willing to provide information. Many districts have societies which concentrate on local history. Other groups can help with research on specialist subjects, such as conservation issues, and the arts.

When researching an unfamiliar city use maps and guidebooks to pinpoint the sights. A stills camera can give you a record of locations, from small shops to busy city streets.

Project Notebook

DOCUMENTARIES

Everyone and everything has a story, in fact, several stories, and each story has a beginning, a middle and an end. The purpose of making a documentary is to select which story you are going to tell, and then to decide how best to tell it. Stories unfold by setting up questions in the viewer's mind and then answering them. Where is this happening? – In this convent. Who is involved? – These are the main characters. As always, research time is never wasted.

■ Use your location. If it is an attractive old building, let the camera linger. If it is a busy scene like a bustling market, pick out details and individuals.

■ Establish the main characters early in the video. It is no good, for instance, to devote the first five minutes of tape to a character who never appears again. In many documentary situations, the characters themselves can form the narrative structure of the piece.

■ Remember the viewer, the end-user of your work. You might get carried away by a particular situation or conversation, but does the audience really want to watch five minutes of the cook explaining how to chop carrots?

■ All videos have an internal sense of pace and rhythm, so it's up to you to impose the pace you want and which suits the subject matter you're covering.

■ React to the moment. If something unexpected happens, shoot it. If it doesn't look good on playback, you can always abandon it.

■ Before going on location, check your equipment thoroughly. To run out of battery power at a crucial moment is unforgivable – and frustrating.

■ Always get the appropriate permissions. If someone finds you shooting on their property without advance warning, they're entitled to be annoyed.

Creating Atmosphere

So far, the video projects examined in this book have been concerned with recording real events. In other words, they have been documentaries of one kind or another. But since cameras are just as useful for creating fictional work, it will not be long before the amateur video maker wants to try his or her hand at making a drama. This chapter therefore examines some of the techniques for this kind of filming. The two major projects used to illustrate these techniques are a short ghost story set in a churchyard and a thriller set in a modern apartment.

Basic Procedures

Since most television dramas eat up large budgets and use huge crews, you might not think that you have much chance of creating a decent fictional work with just a few friends and a camera. But it's certainly possible to create some extremely slick, entertaining productions.

Your first requirement is a script. This need not be complex, but should contain an interesting, coherent narrative, continuously prompting the audience to ask itself what happens next (if inspiration fails, you can always adopt a plot line from a television programme). The story should contain elements of suspense, which resolve themselves at the denouement of the piece.

Imagine what a fairly basic plot will look like on screen. For instance, you could opt for a story with a surprise ending involving a woman being shown alone in her own home. Suddenly she hears an intruder. She is clearly agitated as the footsteps approach the door of her room. The suspense mounts. At this point you have several options. Either you can select an unpleasant ending, or alternatively you could reveal the intruder not to be a murderer but her husband, sneaking home to give her a surprise present.

Atmosphere is created in a number of ways.

First, it depends upon location. There are a number of obvious backdrops which keep appearing in films, and for very good reasons. An old rambling mansion is a traditional setting for thrillers and instantly provides the necessary atmosphere – signalling to the audience that it is in for a rough ride. A run-down inner-city housing block is an equally good setting when creating a different sense of menace. Alternatively, you can use an 'ordinary' location, injecting it with the required atmosphere by the imaginative use of set design and props.

Lighting is also important, particularly when shooting interiors. A soft, warm light tends to create a mellow, peaceful atmosphere. Dim or contrasty lighting with deep shadowy areas suggests menace and suspense. And between these two extremes, there are many other effects that can be achieved by lighting.

Finally, your camerawork and editing style are also vital means of conveying mood and atmosphere. Extreme, unusual camera angles are commonly used in thrillers. Furthermore, during editing, shots can be juxtaposed for extra effects, and the pace with which cuts are made from one scene to another will help propel the film to its climax.

1: A scene from the ghost story project, which is set in a churchyard. The ghostly lady's make-up was achieved by using face whitener. A tungsten white balance was set manually to give an overall blue tint to the shots.

2: Costumes are an excellent way of emphasizing a sense of period and are worth hiring for your video dramas. Alternatively, search amongst local sales for old clothes and outfits that can be adapted to your needs.

3: When filming on location, scrutinize everything that appears in the frame. The last thing you want in a video set in the nineteenth century is the background appearance of a modern house, or even a television aerial! Surprisingly, such errors even occur in professional films. In this instance the wall has just shut out the intrusion of the twentieth century.

4: Scout the location thoroughly, to discover which aspects most effectively convey the atmosphere you require. The churchyard seen through the tangled woods proved to be a highly effective shot.

1: The male character enters the churchyard carrying flowers. Framing the shot through foliage in the foreground cleverly increases the atmosphere and heightens our expectations.

2: The man is first seen at the graveside in a long-shot. Then the camera moves in to a hold the character in mid-shot.

Ghost Story 1

The plot outline for the ghost story is very simple. A man enters a graveyard and kneels at a graveside, perhaps that of his fiancée or wife. Perhaps it is the anniversary of her death. Suddenly, he catches sight of a figure in the distance. He recognizes it as his loved one. He pursues her across the churchyard and into the church, whereupon she approaches a stone figure and vanishes into it. Whilst this plot is by no means Edgar Allan Poe, it doesn't mean that it won't succeed well, and it's a good vehicle for trying out some interesting techniques.

The first step is to translate the basic outline into a shooting script, which will describe each scene in detail, shot-by-shot. The opening image will establish the scene and set the atmosphere. It begins with the churchyard seen in long-shot through the trees. A slow pan follows, providing greater detail, building up the atmosphere and coming to rest on the churchyard gate. This leads to the entrance of the male character.

At this moment the audience instinctively asks: Who is he? and, Why is he there? The first question remains unanswered (you needn't clarify every point in a mystery), but as the camera shows him approaching the grave, the answer to the second is provided. A close-up of the gravestone inscription reveals that it is the grave of a young woman. The expression on the actor's face indicates that he is not merely paying his formal respects, but that there is a deeper sadness.

Up to this point, very little has actually happened. The atmosphere has been created by the location, the slow movements of the camera, and by the use of long-shots. Now, at last, the close-up on the gravestone and the actor reveals more specific information to the audience. And the video's pace increases when the actor sees the ghostly figure of the young woman, first glimpsed fleetingly, as if it were a momentary hallucination.

3: The first reaction shot. The character sees something which shocks him. The audience's pulses are also quickened as they try to find out what it is.

4: The question is answered. The camera goes to a mid-shot of the ghostly figure framed in a gap between the pillars. This shot was cut during editing to make it appear on the screen only for a second or so, to add shock value and impact.

5: The end of the first sequence. The ghostly figure is seen to turn and run. A smoke bomb provides the sudden 'mist'.

Ghost Story 2

1: The ghost figure moving in the churchyard is shown mainly in long-shot to retain a sense of distance and mystery. A big close-up would make her appear too obviously flesh and blood.

2: By cutting shots of the woman standing still during the editing stage with shots of her running, an extra supernatural effect is added: the ghost appears to be in two places at once.

3: For the first time the man and the woman appear in the same shot. With the man standing still and looking at the figure, the pace of this sequence slows down. Now the audience has an opportunity to study each figure in more detail.

The shots on these pages are taken from what might be regarded as the key sequence of the short ghost story. Most of the action develops here, with your priority being to cover these events in such a way as to maintain the atmosphere of suspense created in the earlier sequences.

The great temptation with this sequence is to allow the action to develop too quickly. This would be a mistake, undermining the mood achieved by the earlier coverage, and unreal. For ghosts do not, on the whole, run vigorously like athletes, but glide and reappear mysteriously. Consequently, coverage of the ghostly figure moving through the churchyard was in two basic styles: long-shots of the figure moving around the tombstones, and close-ups of her face when she turns to face the male character. These different shots can be cut together during the editing stage to provide an extra degree of pace.

The first part of this scene keeps the two characters separate. Now, as the climax of the action approaches, they appear in the same frame together for the first time, the woman seen from over the man's shoulder. As the camera goes into close-up on the woman, this becomes a point-of-view shot, seen from the man's perspective. The close-up is held for longer than that in the previous sequence. Next, the camera crabs round the action to give a reaction shot of the man. This shot is held until he speaks to the ghostly figure, whereupon she runs away.

In order to convey an immediate change of pace, and a new section of action, the camera suddenly cuts to the chase across the graveyard in long-shot.

The next scene cuts to the interior of the church, to show the entrance of the woman. For the time being it is important to maintain the pace established in the preceding shots. A drastic slowing of the action would appear unnatural.

The change of location makes the audience ask why she is now in the church. What will she (and we) find there? You can gradually use this expectation to resume a slower pace. A pan shot around the inside of the building (perhaps taken from a low angle to add a sense of strangeness) will achieve this, as well as providing an establishing shot of the new location.

4: Following the pause, the chase begins again. Try to make the action happen as suddenly as possible on screen, to enhance the change of pace of the video.

5: This section of the video ends with a new location: inside the church. Remember that the actress should be seen to enter at roughly the same speed that she approached the building to preserve continuity of pace between the two scenes.

Ghost Story 3

The climax, or denouement, of the story needs careful treatment if it is to create the required impact on the audience. The ending is mysterious, not violent, so it is atmosphere that needs to be built up during the final sequences, not pace.

Following a slow pan around the interior of the church, the camera shows first the woman approaching a monument in one of the recesses. The next shot shows the man entering the church to pause by the door and watch her. The camera then follows the direction of his gaze. The shot should then be held, so that the audience is placed in the man's position, observing the actions of the ghost. Now she slowly turns to face the camera.

At this point the story requires the ghost to 'disappear' and merge into the monument. Without the aid of a Hollywood special-effects department, we need to improvise the best we can. The shot is achieved by gradually losing focus on the woman, framed in a mid-shot. A second shot, taken from the same camera position, but the woman absent, was then filmed. Again the shot is defocused, so it

1: The woman approaches the monument in the recess. Framing the shot with the font in the foreground gives the impression that the man is overlooking the scene.

2: The man stands to one side and observes the scene. His position allows further coverage of the woman from his viewpoint.

will look very similar to the end of the last shot, we then gradually bring the monument into focus.

This is now followed by shots of the man approaching the monument. A final close-up reveals that the statue bears a strong resemblance to the ghost, and an inscription which mirrors that shown earlier on the gravestone. The closing shots are of the man standing in front of the monument, receding into a long-shot, followed by an exterior of the church with the door open, again gradually receding into a long-shot which mirrors the opening of the video.

When preparing to shoot even such a basic project as this, allocate more time than you think you will need. With outdoor locations there is always the possibility of the weather preventing any shooting at all – and with this particular project bright sunshine would have made it more difficult to achieve a supernatural atmosphere. Each shot will have to be rehearsed several times and, quite probably repeated for the camera, before you get it just as you had visualized at the planning stage.

Remember also that actors and helpers may not share your complete enthusiasm, so don't work them too hard. Plan for adequate breaks during the day. A contented crew is much more likely to work overtime than one that's been harassed throughout a long day on an empty stomach.

3: This shot shows the woman going out of focus before she disappears. You must remember the crop for this shot exactly, so that it can be matched when framing up the statue for the next shot.

4: This shot uses the same technique as the last, except in reverse. The statue starts out completely out of focus, and is gradually brought into sharpness using the manual focus controls of the camcorder.

5: The final interior shots show the man standing in front of the monument, absorbed by it. As the camera crabs round behind him it shows the audience what he has been studying. He realizes that the ghost was the statue come to life.

Lighting Interiors

With outdoor locations, you have minimum control over the lighting conditions. Recording indoors is a different matter. However, while you can quite easily use most cameras inside a building using existing light, the resulting images often have a flat, amateurish look to them. In order to achieve the polished images seen on television, you must therefore use supplementary lighting.

In the following project we reveal how to tackle a thriller shot inside a small apartment. The lighting arrangement was introduced first to create a 'natural' look and, second, to complement the tense atmosphere of the plot.

Since 'natural' lighting in video is anything but natural, the sense of flatness has to be overcome by directing lights at the characters, so 'lifting' them from their background. The problem is that when this is achieved with only a single light, large areas of contrast are produced. The light effectively acts as a 'spot'. If a second light is added, the situation is improved, but again there will be large areas of deep shadow. A third light is therefore required to 'lift' the subject from its background and create even lighting.

The system is known as three-point lighting. The first light is called the key-light, and is placed at a slight angle to the front of the subject. The second light is known as the fill. It is positioned to the other side of the subject, usually at a slightly greater angle, and relieves the shadowy areas created by the key. The third light is the backlight, positioned behind the subject, casting a slight rimming effect which helps to lift the subject from the background (see page 50 for more information about this set-up). On set, each light can be arranged so that it performs two functions – one character's key-light acts as another's fill.

The positioning of lights on a set is a matter of trial and error. There are no absolute rules. The lighting must be even across the entire area where the action takes place and, of course, it must be hidden from the camera during any particular shot. This means planning camera and lighting positions in advance, and/or hiding the lights on set (lights can be hidden behind any opaque surface on set, such as a lace curtained window or a picture frame). You may also need to use reflectors (for example, large sheets of white card or pieces of white expanded polystyrene) to bounce the light to the place where you need it. Reflectors can be useful if your budget is limited and you do not have enough lights.

1: Three-point lighting is used in this shot, in which both characters are fully lit and lifted from the background. The resultant shadowy areas appear entirely natural.

2: In this shot, the effect of the key-light can be seen clearly. The fill is less powerful, so there some shadow on the right side of the girl's face. The effect helps to concentrate the viewer's attention on the girl.

3: With no additional lighting, this shot would appear flat on the screen. The highlights on the girl's hair give the shot added visual intensity.

4: Remember that the lighting effect will vary with the position of the camera. If you shoot from an unusual angle, check the lighting conditions, both directly and through the camera's viewfinder, or on a separate TV monitor.

Building Tension

In a thriller the intention is to keep the audience on the edge of its seat, whether or not the audience is in a packed cinema or in your own front room. In other words, the audience should constantly be aware that something unpleasant is likely to occur. To achieve this expectancy, the plot should develop shot by shot, building up to a climax. Timing is therefore more important in this than in any other type of video.

Although the tension should be inherent in the script, it is the video maker's responsibility to exploit this to the full. One of the most useful devices for achieving this is the point-of-view shot, which places the audience in the position of one of the screen characters. So, in this particular project, when the audience sees the door handle ominously turning, it sees it from the point of view of the heroine who, in the last shot, is looking anxiously towards the door. Thus the previous shot establishes the meaning of the subsequent one – without the look of anxiety in the actress's eyes, the door handle would convey no sinister meaning at all, it would simply be another feature of the room.

The opposite of the point-of-view shot is one in which the audience is presented with information which it knows the characters in the drama are unaware of. This could be achieved by juxtaposing two different sequences running simultaneously – a technique called parallel action. A typical example would involve showing a woman relaxing in her home alone. Her behaviour shows that she is unaware of any threat. A second shot shows male feet stealthily climbing a staircase. By cutting between these two shots, the audience assumes the two actions are related – it senses what is about to happen, while the woman remains ignorant, and it awaits the awful moment when she will share the knowledge.

Often, such sequences must be drawn out beyond a natural time scale to be fully effective. Although in real life it only takes a couple of seconds to mount a staircase, an audience will accept a much longer time span as tension is built up. Additional tension can be created by shooting from an unusual angle. An obliquely framed shot automatically suggests the unusual or the bizarre, but it loses its effectiveness if used too often.

1–2: Changing focus from the girl to the approaching man is a good way of building tension in this scene. The unusual, tilted camera angle also increases the sense of menace.

3: A cut to this silhouette gives a sense of the girl's isolation and vulnerability – and also her unawareness of the threat.

4: Shooting tense or violent scenes in close-up concentrates the viewer's mind on the essentials – the facial expressions and the close physical contact between the two people.

5–6: When the telephone rings, the action slows down. The girl's reluctant steps towards the phone and the deliberate way in which she picks it up and holds it increase the audience's sense of expectation.

Editing to Increase Suspense

Narrative comes first and foremost in creating suspense, and it evolves according to the way in which one shot relates to another – that is, according to how they are edited.

The audience will begin watching the thriller video knowing nothing. So before suspense can be created they must be supplied with a basic amount of information. What is the setting? Who are the main characters? What is their relationship? Is it satisfactory? Is there any underlying tension?

As the drama unfolds, so the audience is fed with increasing amounts of information that further define the story. If this flow of information comes too slowly, the audience will become bored. Too fast, and the audience will not be able to assimilate everything it is being told. Each scene should therefore either provide information or pose a question, prompting the audience to consider various aspects of the plot. What will she do now that the man has left her after a blazing row? Who is that on the telephone? Why is she going towards the bathroom?

Gradually, in turn, each answer leads to new questions. Will the man return to the flat in time to call an ambulance and save the girl following her overdose? And if he does, how will her suicide attempt affect their future relationship? Whilst the timing of these questions and answers is the main function of plotting, which is the writer's primary concern, making these questions work on the screen is the central task of the editor, who cuts from scene to scene.

This question-and-answer process should lead up to an inevitable climax in which, in conventional stories, all the conflicting elements and questions in the drama are resolved.

You may, however, prefer a more realistic conclusion, in which there is no obvious solution. But if you chose this ending, remember that your audience may well feel cheated. After all, it is in the very nature of suspense to lead the audience to expect an ending that is conclusive. What is good for one form of video, such as a documentary, is not necessarily good for a thriller.

2: The actor's reaction supplies the answer. The shot tells the audience that he realizes that something is wrong and sets up a second question: what will he do next?

I: The audience knows what the man doesn't – his girlfriend has taken an overdose of sleeping tablets. Shots of the man approaching the flat with a conciliatory bunch of flowers create a sense of anticipation in the audience: what will he do when he discovers the girl unconscious?

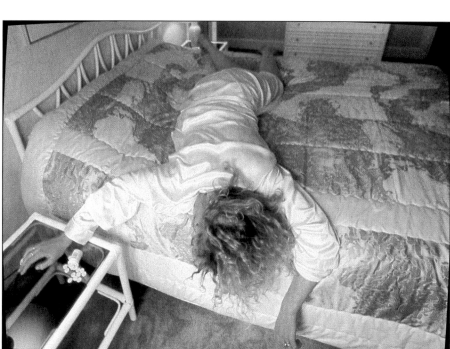

3: Rapid intercutting between what the man sees and the overall scene heightens tension in this section of the video. The first shot shows the girl on the bed – the sight that confronts the man when he enters the room. We may glimpse the pills on the table before the cut to the next shot.

4: The fast cut to the shot of the two figures together shows that the man is acting quickly. Fast action like this keeps up the tempo and the tension.

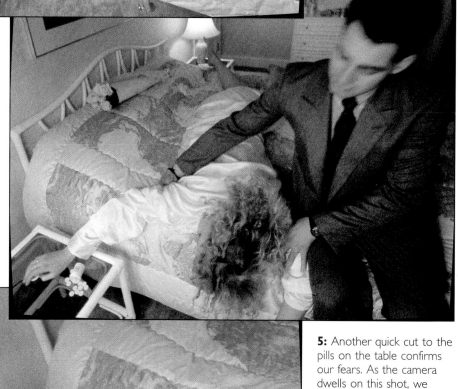

5: Another quick cut to the pills on the table confirms our fears. As the camera dwells on this shot, we wonder whether the girl is alive or not – this time, suspense is increased by the lack of action.

Additional Coverage

1: This is a good example of a telling juxtaposition. The girl is tense, but the repose of the classical sculpture seems to make her even tenser by contrasts. This is part of a sequence in which the girl moves towards the mirror and the camera crabs round slightly to reveal her reflection – another way of underlining the strength of her mood.

When you are filming the frantic action of this type of story, it is all too tempting to dwell on the characters themselves – they are, after all, the main subject, and you are producing a film about their relationship. But a video that consisted solely of mid-shots of the main characters would soon get boring.

As you go along, look out for telling details and small pieces of action that allow you to use your technique to make some sort of comment about what is going on – details of their home that might tell us something about their past, or close-ups at tense points in the drama. You may end up with some isolated shots that you do not actually use, but experimenting will usually provide something that is worth keeping.

Even if you concentrate on isolated shots, bear in mind the potential for intercutting later. A shot of something that reminds us of a character's happy past will give an ironic twist when cut into a sequence about her unhappy present life. Such shots could just be used as cutaways to smooth over a cut at the editing stage. Above all, be observant, and do not be afraid to shoot too much.

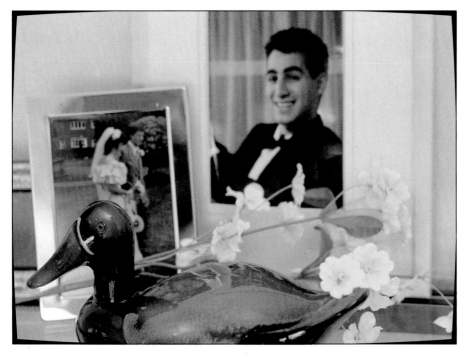

2: Images from the past can have a powerful effect. Here, relaxed photographs create an ironic backdrop to the turbulent life that makes up the subject of most of the video.

3–5: In this sequence details provide tension and ambiguity right up to the last second. The quiet apartment, the approaching hand, and then the two figures – but it is a moment before we find out whether the outcome will be a fight or a passionate embrace.

Continuity

The art of video making lies in maintaining the illusion that the image on the screen is a part of reality. Any mistake you make in continuity (the consistency of details from one scene to the next) will be picked up by the audience, and the illusion will be destroyed.

Continuity is most obviously lost when aspects of the actors' costumes change unaccountably between shots, or a prop is moved between scenes for no apparent reason. The only guarantee of maintaining continuity is meticulous attention to detail. If, in a previous shot, an actress is shown wearing shoes, she must not be shown barefooted in the following shot. An ashtray that was overflowing at the beginning shouldn't be pristine later

on. In general, try to avoid situations that might give rise to continuity problems – if there is no reason for your characters to smoke, don't have them smoking. No matter how small the detail, the audience *will* notice. To ensure that props are not touched, declare the shooting area a total no-go area when shooting is not in progress.

In professional video someone is usually delegated to check for elements of continuity. You will probably have to do the job yourself.

A good practice, particularly if there has been a long break in shooting, is to review the preceding shot before setting up the new one. Close attention to continuity will at least ensure that you consider composition too.

1: As well as the girl's mood, we notice minor details such as the fact she is still wearing her dressing gown when the man arrives.

2: A cut to the reconciliation scene, with the girl fully dressed, signals to the audience that some time has passed since the last shot.

3–4: A brief glimpse of the man leaving shows him wearing a jacket now. Even this tiny error of continuity before the cut to a big close-up of the girl could attract the audience's attention.

5–6: Intercutting between shots of the girl wearing different outfits will really confuse the viewer.

185

Project Notebook

DRAMA

Drama is the glamorous end of video making – everyone wants to be Steven Spielberg. But even with limited resources and a budget that consists of little more than the change in your pocket you can create an interesting, absorbing product. The first requirement is a script that works: it must be ingenious enough to have inherent interest, but it must also be conceived within the limitations to which you are working. The video maker's job is to translate the words on the page into images on the screen in the most effective way.

■ Finding a good location is half the battle – it is easier to be spooky in an old churchyard than it is in a supermarket.

■ In drama, particularly suspense drama, it is essential that as soon as the audience has been given the answer to one narrative question, another is posed.

■ Pacing the plot is everything.

■ Obscure and unusual camera angles *do* add a disturbing sense to the image on the screen, but, used too often, they simply antagonize the audience and lose their effect. Be selective about their use.

■ The audience must believe that what it is watching is real. Simple continuity errors destroy this conspiracy between you and the audience.

■ Select camera angles and movements before you begin to shoot. Let the action happen in front of the lens, don't chase it.

■ An imaginative use of simple props and set decorations can add greatly to the effectiveness of the video.

Shooting Action

Video recordings of sports events demand particular techniques because the action being captured often happens at high speed, or at a distance. In addition, each kind of sport demands its own individual approach. Baseball, for instance, can be shot from one or two static camera positions, whereas golf demands far greater mobility for proper coverage.

This chapter examines these various considerations, taking in camera positions and shooting techniques for field and track sports. It also provides invaluable suggestions for extending and applying these techniques to other kinds of video work, and looks at the preparations you should make before going on an 'action' shoot.

One-Chance Action

In sports, such as horse racing, canoeing and skiing, where the action is channelled once only along a set course, you must ensure that you get the right shot first time. If you fail, there's no second chance. You must therefore put a great deal of effort into visualizing the event beforehand, so that there is no risk whatsoever of your being unprepared.

You should also try to envisage how the action may not go according to plan, so that you are ready to tackle the unexpected. The last thing you want is to be incorrectly positioned at a highly dramatic moment so that the camera misses it.

This video of white-water canoeing reveals ways of ensuring that you overcome any problems that might prevent you from filming one-chance action successfully, and also how to tackle many extra considerations.

The first problem was deciding where best to film from because the river banks were covered in thick undergrowth. Eventually, after much thought, four fixed points were chosen: the start; a bridge over a straight section of river; a bend near the road; and the finishing point, 1 mile (1.6km) downstream.

Although the canoeists moved fast, test runs revealed that manual focusing gave a better result than the autofocus because it was too easily confused by other foreground objects, including heavy spray hanging in the air.

1–2: High-speed slaloming between upright poles in turbulent water is one of the main skills of this sport. The most advantageous camera position for capturing this particular moment was by a river bend. As the canoeists hold their position whilst they manoeuvre between the poles, it's possible to obtain good mid-shots using the zoom.

CHECKLIST

■ Study the map for good vantage points for shooting.
■ Check that access to these positions is readily available.
■ Establish the significant points of action in the event.
■ Time how long it takes to get from one location to another.
■ Make sure you have spare batteries and tapes.

3: For a dramatic start, take high-angle shots of the canoeists racing away from you.

4: This following sequence, shot from the road bridge, begins with the canoeists approaching the camera 'head on'. The shot begins at the telephoto end of the zoom lens and is 'held' as the canoeists approach.

5: Here the camera position lets you film the canoeists approaching the 'line', before panning to show each canoe passing by you as they cross the finish. Since the pan should be quick, you should be close to the action for a short camera movement.

1: American football is one of the most thrilling and colourful of sports. This shot was taken from the sidelines, about one-third of the way down the pitch. From this angle, you get a sense of immediacy, but much of the pattern of play may be obscured by the players.

2–3: The tennis court is on a smaller scale than a football field, so you will be more able to get closer shots of the players.

Pitch and Court Coverage

Sports events such as tennis, American football and basketball, which take place on a court or field, present different problems to the video maker. Such games are distinguished by there being opposing players or teams in which the *direction* of play is important, so creating problems in trying to avoid 'crossing the line'. Fortunately, the action occurs in a fixed arena, so the camera positions can avoid this problem.

There are two basic camera positions (where you will need to use a tripod) for covering such events: side-on to the line of play, and behind it. These positions will provide full coverage of what is happening. If you use more than two positions

the viewer is liable to lose a coherent sense of space and direction.

However, if you are only going to record snatches of play, you can adopt extra camera positions, so enabling you to show, for example, 10 minutes recorded from the centre of the right-hand touch-line, followed by another sequence from behind the goal-line. But remember that if you move from the right side of the court to the left, you will effectively change the direction of play on screen. Such a change of shot would confuse the viewer hopelessly, particularly since in field and court sports players often change ends periodically throughout the game.

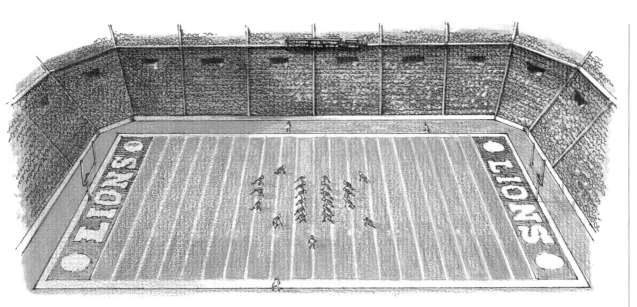

Camera position 3 allows you to get good shots of action along the sidelines and in the deep zone.

Camera position 1, on the half-way line, allows good overall coverage and is ideally placed for the kick-off and for general, wide-angle shots showing mid-field play.

Camera position 2, behind the goal, will give good coverage of goal shots and attacking play in the mid-field. Don't forget to turn and record the spectators' excitement.

4: A head-on shot of the quarterback about to make a play. The shot was taken from position 2, using the telephoto end of the zoom — notice the compressed out-of-focus background.

5: A zoom-in shot taken from position 3 when the action was on the same side of the pitch as the camera.

6: This shot was taken from the half-way line, but from a raised position in the stand. This gives a better overall view of the game than a similar shot taken from pitch level.

1–2: The opening sequence shows the land-yachts and the competitors preparing their vehicles for the race. This gives the opportunity for some dramatic shots of the land-yachts outlined against the sky.

3–4: This is succeeded by shots of the vehicles moving out on to the track for practice runs.

Setting the Scene

With unfamiliar sports and activities, it is important to introduce the audience to the nature of the event so that it is not totally lost.

The coverage on this spread is taken from a video of a land-yachting meeting. The film begins with an interesting section on land-yachts being assembled by the competitors. The early part of the meeting and film therefore features the preparation of and final checks to these vehicles. Shots of the competitors talking and exchanging jokes as they fine tune their machines contribute to a lively opening sequence.

These sequences are also useful for introducing the principles of the sport. The sound commentary allows the competitors to explain that they race against each other and the clock, increasing speed by skilfully tacking with the wind in the same way as do nautical yachtsmen. The event takes place on the runways of a small airfield, where the prevailing wind conditions enable competitors to reach top speeds in excess of 40mph.

Another bonus of this early coverage is that it provides an opportunity to feature selected competitors. This gives the sequence a focus, and provides subsequent sequences of the race with extra dramatic impact as viewers follow the competitors' progress. But while setting the scene is a vital part of the film, do not dwell on it for too long. After all, the video you are making is one of a land-yachting *race*, not a documentary about the lives and thoughts of land-yachting devotees.

Since the coverage should be paced to give a sense of the build-up to the race, it's a good idea to interview some of the contestants. Ask them how they rate their chances? How nervous do they feel? Who they think are their main rivals? Have they ever had any nasty crashes?

The more you can inject a sense of the anxieties and hopes of the participants, the more the audience will watch the video in these terms, waiting to see whether their aspirations are fulfilled, or their fears confirmed. In other words, the race should be converted into a human drama. Without this element, you are dependent on an exciting race with a close finish which may not necessarily happen.

This sequence could conclude with shots of competitors putting on their crash helmets and climbing into their yachts to indicate that the race is about to begin.

CHECKLIST

■ Establish who are the competitors, and ask them to talk about their sport.
■ Film the full range of preparations (including checking the yacht and examining the course) before the event begins.
■ Decide on which aspects of the sport you wish to concentrate, and plan your camera positions accordingly.

5: A second short sequence shows the land-yachtsmen grouping by the starting line. Their light bantering as they get ready for the race reinforces the sense of camaraderie and friendly rivalry.

6: The camera moved in to isolate and identify individuals and their yachts, so that the viewer can follow their progress during the race. If you don't manage to include the winner at this stage, it will be necessary to try to get this shot after the race.

7: When the race itself is in progress, you will have little time to think about unusual or interesting camera angles and shots. The comparatively calm moments as the competitors prepare themselves is the time when such shots are best attempted. This shot along the plane of the yacht's sail adds both visual variety and gives the viewer a good impression of scale.

Set Pieces

Many games have important set pieces within the course of play – for example, the service in tennis, the line-out in rugby football, and the pitch in baseball. Since these set pieces are often the most dramatic moments of the game, a sports video should feature them, particularly if the video is only going to contain highlights.

Because the play is temporarily held up at this point, the video maker will have extra time in which to set up the shot. This can often give you a great opportunity to zoom in for close-ups of the key players, to help vary the visual pace of the video and give a sense of individual competition.

Depending on your position, the camera may have to pan quickly to capture an exciting moment following on from a set piece, for which a smooth tripod action will be invaluable. This is particularly useful in such games as ice hockey and soccer where you need to follow fast action. As an alternative, follow the set piece using the zoom lens.

As when making any video, however, try to minimize sweeping camera movements as much as possible – a side-on tennis video shot which goes back and forth between the two players would soon instil a feeling approaching seasickness in the viewer. Keeping the camera still has one particular advantage, in that it helps give an authentic feeling that the viewer is a 'live' spectator of the action.

1: In tennis, the basic set piece in the action is the serve. The player takes up position on the baseline, so framing is relatively simple. The shot was taken from a high angle, slightly in front of the baseline.

2: American football is almost all set-piece play. At the beginning of each play, the opposing forwards line up against each other. This shot was taken from the sidelines, using the telephoto end of the zoom, to catch the big crunch when the ball is played.

3: Baseball is a comparatively stationary game, and hence provides good opportunities for set-piece coverage. The pitcher throws from a fixed position, so it is easy to frame this action. Similarly, you could concentrate on the batsman, who also remains still while waiting for the delivery.

4–5: Ice hockey and soccer are more fluid games, so coverage must be more free-ranging. However, both contain penalty hits or kicks, and these can be treated as set pieces. These shots are perhaps best taken from behind the goal, facing the direction of the action.

Track and Circuit Action

Returning to the land-yachting video, you can see that the action takes place on a track, as it does in athletic track events and in motor sport. In this case, the track is a long oval with sharp corners. Having set the scene with informal coverage of the pre-race activities, it is now necessary to decide from which parts of the track the shots of the race should be taken.

Obviously there have to be shots of the start and finish, and of the most spectacular aspects of the race. These include the land-yachts cornering, which they do at speed, keeling over so dramatically that only two wheels touch the ground – a crash being prevented only by the yachtsman's fine sense of balance.

The course is just 1 mile (1.6 km) long. With this kind of coverage it is important to keep a sense of direction on the screen – any apparent reversal of direction of the land-yachts, caused by switching to different camera positions on the other side of the track, would ruin the coverage. When the cameras are moved, great care must therefore be taken to switch from the outside of the track on the outward circuit to the inside of the track on the opposite side.

The track layout with camera positions and some of the types of shots that can be achieved are shown here. It is actually worth drawing a sketch or map of the track to work out your camera positions in advance of the day of the shoot itself.

1–3: The position at the top corner of the track provides good, almost head-on coverage of the yachts gathering speed down the straight. This also produces exciting shots of the yachts doing 'wheelies'. Although the vehicles appear to be on the point of going out of control, there are no major upsets.

5: By taking up a camera position at the far end of the circuit, you will obtain excellent footage of the land-yachts racing down the home straight.

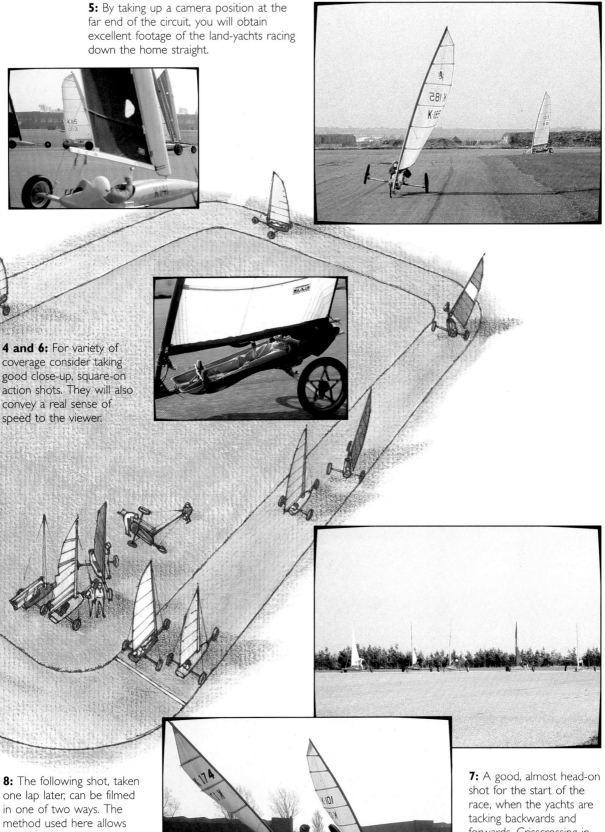

4 and 6: For variety of coverage consider taking good close-up, square-on action shots. They will also convey a real sense of speed to the viewer.

8: The following shot, taken one lap later, can be filmed in one of two ways. The method used here allows the yacht to approach the bend and then move around it out of shot as the other competitors approach.

7: A good, almost head-on shot for the start of the race, when the yachts are tacking backwards and forwards. Crisscrossing in this way enables the yachts to take full advantage of the prevailing wind. This particular shot will be held until the yachts are so near that they are almost in close-up.

Day of Action

Sports and action coverage, no matter what the subject, has one common element: movement – and usually movement at speed. Perhaps the most popular situation in which to begin exploring the techniques of action coverage is at a school sports day. The subjects will usually be friends and family, so the video will have a guaranteed audience which will be interested to watch it.

Athletics comprises of track and field events. In track events, the action takes place over a large area, so you will need to select camera positions which provide you with the best view of what is going on. The techniques for doing this are dealt with in another part of the chapter. Field events, such as throwing the javelin, or the high jump, take place in a limited area. This means it is relatively easy to select a safe camera position from which you can get good coverage of individual performances.

Remember, to convey the full atmosphere of the day, you should also get shots away from the action – parents greeting their children after a race, the presentation of the prizes, and the picnic in the school grounds afterwards.

2–4: A head-on view of the action give a better view of all the runners at once.

1: Side-on views of track events tell the viewer the most important thing they wish to know: who's in the lead. You can choose to concentrate on the battle for the lead, or perhaps concentrate on an individual athlete.

5–7: Field events present fewer problems. You can record the throw or jump from a fixed position. With practice, it is possible to follow the flight of the javelin through the air.

8: The glittering prizes. Coverage of the presentation of prizes allows you both to record the overall scene and obtain close-ups of individual competitors.

Different Approaches

1: In swimming, it is relatively easy to track an individual's performance, and to frame the shots in mid-shot to allow later analysis of performance. In particularly bright conditions outdoors, you need to use a polarizing filter to cut down glare from the water. Remember that indoor swimming pools cause problems with the acoustics, so the soundtrack may well be too distorted to listen to – dub in a commentary later.

2: The classic shot for skateboarding is to use a wideangle converter and shoot from the top of the bowl, using a video light for fill-in. It can be dangerous though!

3: In all sports, including boxing, video can be a very useful tool for training. It allows the sportsman and the trainer to analyse the mistakes in slow motion.

There is, of course, no limit to the types of action event you can cover. Analyse the event in terms of whether it is a team game, or an individual sport, whether it is engaged in a large or small area, and in terms of the equipment and resources you have at your disposal to obtain coverage.

The shots shown on these pages are taken from a number of sources. The coverage of the sumo wrestling, a traditional Japanese sport surrounded by complex ritual and ceremony, is more in the area of documentary footage. For most viewers, the rules of the sport are secondary to the spectacle of the giant wrestlers, and their preparations are as fascinating as the actual wrestling itself.

Such considerations are really an anticipation of audience interest. If your tape is going to be watched by sports professionals, or by avid followers of the game you are covering, then they will tend to appreciate colourful asides from the action rather less. Analysis of the game becomes your prime aim.

A less knowledgeable audience will be more interested in the overall atmosphere, and the background to what's going on – so it is helpful to use interviews with participants to help convey the principles of the game being played.

4–5: This sumo wrestling was shot in a training camp during a trip to Japan. The wrestling itself takes place in a small ring, and each bout is fast and furious, usually over in seconds. Shoot in long-shot to avoid missing the main action, which usually involves one or two of these heavyweights falling out of the ring.

6–7: For most non-Japanese, sumo wrestling remains a somewhat bizarre spectacle. The coverage was not particularly selective, since almost all of what was going on in the training hall was fascinating.

1: This shot shows the trainer in action with a group of potential land-yachters. This kind of coverage can be useful to show to other beginners to give a general grounding in the sport.

Video Training

One of the major reasons for making a video of a sports event is to use it as a coaching aid. Individual performances can be reviewed and analyzed in detail, using the slow motion and freeze-frame functions of the VCR. Professional players make great use of such video recordings to study their own and their opponents' games.

If you are going to make a coaching video, how should you approach the task? In many cases, individuals are concerned about a particular aspect of their game. They will tell you, for example, that their backswing, when driving a golf ball, is creating terrible problems.

Although fast shutter speed settings on camcorders are of little use for most types of video, they come into their own for sports training. If the video is shot with a fast shutter speed it will be less blurred when replayed in slow motion, or when held on freeze frame. However, as most camcorders have only rudimentary tape transport controls, you will have to transfer the tape to a VHS video recorder with these facilities.

If you are unfamiliar with the techniques of the game in question, you may have to ask for a quick run down on the most important aspects. When you know exactly on which area of his or her game the player wants to concentrate, shoot it over and over again. Take long-shots, highlighting the player's posture and balance. Then shoot close-ups of particular parts of the body: the feet

2–4: By strategic placement of the camera, it is possible to study technique at key moments. In land-yachting, these include the art of keeping the yacht upright whilst cornering.

5: Shooting into the sky for this pole vault has its own special problems. Here the camera must be very carefully positioned in order to get maximum coverage whilst avoiding glare from the sun.

6: If you wish to record your own performance, you will have to set up the camera in advance and place markers to indicate the positions you should take up while practising. In this case, this simply means head on to the hurdler.

7: A strategic moment in canoeing technique involves this manoeuvre through the poles beside the bank.

to record stance, and the hands to show grip. Next, record the player from different angles: head-on, from side-on, and from behind. If the player is trying out alternative techniques, record these too. And finally, to ensure that you can study the tape without any distractions, use a tripod to avoid camera shake.

Such coverage is fine if the player is more or less stationary, as in golf or pool, but an athlete may want to study his or her performance over the full 400m of the track. In this case you could set up camera positions around the circuit as described in Track and Circuit Action, shooting from each point on separate occasions if necessary.

Project Notebook

SPORTS

Sports coverage is a specialized area of video, requiring special skills and quick reaction times. Since you have only one chance to capture the action, there's no room for mistakes – you can hardly ask them to run the Olympic 100 metres again, just because you forgot to remove the lens cap! You should also immerse yourself in the sport that you are going to cover, in order that you will be able to anticipate how the action is likely to develop.

■ Selecting the best camera positions before the action begins is the single most effective way of ensuring that you get full, informative coverage.

■ Remember that in many games, switching camera positions from one side of the action to the other is going to confuse the audience. By crossing the line, it appears that you have reversed the direction of play on screen.

■ Close-ups are effective, but it is more important to leave the audience with a clear sense of the play as a whole.

■ Sport doesn't happen in a vacuum. Set the scene beforehand: cover the competitors preparing for the event, the spectators arriving – all the razzmatazz.

■ Video comes into its own as a training tool. Co-operate with the player to analyse his or her game in full, then replay the results, using freeze-frame to pick out details.

■ The accidental and the unexpected happen every day in sport. Such coverage always has great audience interest and is worth duplicating for a compilation tape.

■ The spectators are an intrinsic part of any sports event, creating the unique atmosphere. Remember to get some shots of spectators' reactions, perhaps during breaks in the play.

Additional Resources

As you master the camcorder, so the number of subjects you can successfully film greatly increases. One particularly exciting and challenging project is the progress of an amateur theatrical production from its earliest days on. This not only provides an entertaining record of a lively, evolving group activity, but also enables you to acquire a wide range of important skills – including directing two or more cameras and working with a team.

The latter is a highly worthwhile experience because there will be a few occasions when you can work surrounded by and controlling lighting technicians, make-up artists, props buyers, script editors, producers, and so on. The theatre project is therefore also an excellent, albeit very gentle, introduction to the professional world of movie makers – George Lucas, Steven Spielberg and all.

Using Two Cameras

By acquiring a second camera and operator you more than double your possibilities for making a video with excellent coverage, and a varied range of camera angles. You will be able to record the action from two different camera positions simultaneously, or have one camera roving while the other takes the basic shots. So, at the editing stage, your options are greatly increased. However, with two cameras at your disposal, you must also think about your approach much more carefully.

Your first criterion is to establish a clear, agreed objective amongst all those working on the video. Is the film to be a recording of the theatre group at work, featuring behind-the-scenes activities and rehearsals, so becoming a semi-documentary? Or is your prime aim to lead up to and highlight the actual performance?

Assuming that you have selected the second option, you should clarify your shooting options. The best time for filming close-up shots of facial reactions and gestures is during the dress rehearsals. This really won't be possible 'on the night' when a camera in front of the stage could disrupt the play or would certainly obstruct the audience's view. During the public performances, the cameras must be unobtrusive.

Your second objective is to set up the cameras in two different positions before recording one performance in its entirety. These two tapes will provide most of the material that you will require for the final edited recording.

Choosing the camera positions depends, to a large extent, on the layout of the theatre. For example, if there is a balcony, make the most of this high viewpoint, which will provide an excellent alternative to one right in front of the action. It can also be used for those moments when a personal drama subsides, and we see the characters in a wider perspective. Or, commence the action from high up, revealing the set and the characters, before closing in as the tension increases.

Another camera position well worth considering is in the wings, at the side of the stage. But do check during rehearsals that props, stage lights, and actors waiting to enter will not obstruct this viewpoint during any point in the play.

1–3: During dress rehearsals, you will be able to get a camera on stage to record close-ups of actors' expressions, to be cut in at the editing stage.

4: Shots taken on stage should not be from too many different angles, as here, otherwise you'll have problems.

5: This shot is taken with the camera placed to the front and just to the right of centre stage (do check that such a position provides a wide enough angle of view). Being close to the action in this way is important for establishing a sense of intimacy, but if you are forced to move the camera too much to follow the action, you will end up sacrificing intimacy for irritating distraction for the actors. In this particular play – *Rookery Nook*, a knock-about farce by Ben Travers – there is a great deal of fast action on stage and so the cameraman would have to be very knowledgeable about the actors' moves to avoid getting in their way.

6: This shot from high up is part of a trial sequence taken from the balcony during dress rehearsals. From here you can use the zoom in close on the players during significant dramatic moments. Mark such points in your script so that you are well prepared for them as the play unfolds. On the whole, shots taken from such a high angle look particularly theatrical. This is not necessarily a bad thing, but it could create problems when you cut to shots from other camera positions.

7: Close-ups should be treated with care and certainly practised at rehearsal. You will need to know exactly what positions the actor will take up and be aware of the course the dialogue takes, so that you can plan shots of character's reactions. Again, remember to keep moves to a minimum, so letting the action develop in front of the camera and tell its own story. Another point to bear in mind is that some of the actors are going to make more interesting subjects than others for close-ups. The actor in the centre of this trio was perfect – playing the stool pigeon, he had a marvellously expressive face.

1: The director is the linchpin of any production, providing creative stimulus as well as practical support to the cast and to the video crew.

The Director

A video production with a team of helpers, no matter how small, needs someone in control, someone to provide direction and to allow specialist members of the crew to pursue their own tasks. In other words, someone needs to be the director.

In some Hollywood legends the director is a tyrannical, creative monster. But try imitating that severe style with friends and you'll soon be the only person on the project!

The ideal director therefore combines an overall creative vision of the project with fastidious attention to detail, and tact, humour and diplomacy when managing the crew. The director must also be efficient and organized, but sufficiently flexible to change plans when the unexpected happens (as it inevitably does in the unscripted events of life!).

Long before shooting starts, there should be discussions about the aims of the project and a precise allocation of the duties of each team member. The director must not approach these early planning sessions as a general free-for-all discussion. Instead he or she should guide the meetings – having come prepared with a flexible story-

2: Besides being a master of video techniques, the director must also know how to get the cast to adapt their acting techniques for the camera. The most important elements on which to concentrate include conveying emotions through small gestures, such as a sudden, darting eye movement, or a raised eyebrow. In a large theatre such gestures could go unnoticed, but provided the camera operator is instructed to home in on them your home video audience will appreciate their significance.

board, shooting scripts and video examples of the type of work he or she is trying to achieve.

It is virtually impossible to give a definitive list of the duties of a director on an amateur video project. But two of the most important involve obtaining good, wide coverage of the event, and selecting specific shots. The camera operators must therefore be given specific briefs that leave nothing to chance. And the director should not be shy of checking his proposed shots through the viewfinder or through video monitors.

One of the most important abilities any director should have is a talent for dealing with people. This means first of all assessing what everyone's strong and weak points are. You will then be able to make best use of the crew, cast and any other helpers you may have at your disposal. Give them tasks that they can perform well and you will not only get the best results possible – everyone will get a certain amount of satisfaction from the project.

You will also have to learn, if it does not come naturally, how to criticize without being too negative. If you are too critical, you will only alienate your cast – and since they are probably only volunteers anyway, this is pointless. So it is usually best to find something in a performance to praise, and allow the actor to build on this, rather than being destructively critical of the parts of a performance you do not like.

The same thing applies to the crew. You will find that you will have to become something of an expert in every area – sound, lighting, stage management and acting – in order to be able to instruct your cast and crew precisely and to keep an overall eye on standards. The more you know, the more you will command respect. But don't

impose your own knowledge for its own sake – each member of the team will have their own suggestions to make and you should try to benefit from these rather than dismissing them automatically in favour of your own.

Directing for the screen

If you are dealing with actors who are used to performing 'live' you will probably have to remind them that theatrical gestures often look exaggerated in front of the camera. This is especially true if you are working in close-up, where often a simple raising of the eyebrow or a slight shrugging of the shoulders is enough to convey the sort of strong emotion that might require a much more emphatic movement in the theatre.

Another difference between theatre and video is that the director should always check the scene as it looks through the camera. You can do this by looking through the viewfinder, of course, but it is better to use video monitors connected to the cameras. The monitors provide a better check on composition than is available through the viewfinder. They also allow you to assess colour balance accurately, even if your camcorder has a built-in LCD screen. It is much the best thing to make these checks as you work – constant repetition of the same sequence will bore the cast and waste a great deal of time.

Once the director has total control of the shooting side of the video, instructing the camera operators and checking proposed shots, he must ensure, with the aid of the lighting technicians, that the lighting conveys the required atmosphere. And finally, on top of all this, the director must just as importantly inspire the cast to perform for the camera, not an audience.

3: Always survey the on-stage area from all possible angles. Whilst the bulk of your coverage will probably be taken from a conventional point of view, it might be useful to obtain additional, more unusual footage in subsequent performances which you can incorporate into the tape at the editing stage.

The Crew

The size of your crew will depend upon the project at hand and the resources at your disposal. For most people, these resources will be minimal, so what is the minimum crew to aim for in a reasonably ambitious video project?

First, there must be someone to operate each camera. While it may be possible for the director to take control of one camera, this will restrict his or her other duties. You will also need someone to control and monitor sound – a vital job, since a poor soundtrack will render all the other work a waste of time.

In addition to these tasks, you will require a general electrician/floor manager. This person will be responsible for everything outside the specialized tasks of the rest of the crew – checking electrical connections, passing messages and offering back-up whenever needed. That makes a total of five – any fewer and even the most basic multi-camera shoot will be running short.

Of course, there are an additional number of particular skills that are extremely useful if available. A set-designer-cum-art-director can help style the whole production. This contribution can be limited to choosing costumes and designing the set, or expanded into creating storyboards in collaboration with the writer/director and choosing locations for outdoor work.

Lighting is another specialist responsibility. If you are working in a fully staffed theatre, there will be lighting staff on hand to achieve the effects required by the video director. Make sure the crew is able to carry out your requirements. But without this support you will need your own electrician/lighting controller. This means that you will have to set up the lighting for each individual scene before it is acted, noting down the levels for each lighting change.

Below: A storyboard is a useful visual aid for the director, even though he or she will be familiar with the play from watching it during rehearsal.

■ **The sound engineer** positions the microphones and monitors the quality of recording throughout each take, and also gives the cue for sound effects.

■ **The lighting supervisor** arranges the lights as required by the director, operating them from the lighting gallery in a theatre.

■ **Camera operator 1** will need to be fully briefed on the shots required (unless the director is filling this role).

■ **Camera operator 2.** This camera can either be in a fixed position, or 'rove' to capture the action from different angles.

■ **The director.** Although he or she is nominally the head of the crew, the best results will be obtained where everyone contributes to the project.

■ **The technician/ manager** co-ordinates all aspects of the production, as well as filling any gaps whenever required.

■ **The cast** is initially the responsibility of the theatrical director, unless he is the same person as the video director. If not, the latter may be allowed to modify the cast's positions and gestures during special shots taken during the rehearsals.

■ **Below:** Each member of the crew should have a copy of the shooting script, marked where they must perform their specific tasks. For camera operators these will principally be indications of change of shot: the introduction of close-ups, or a slow pan, for example. Camera cues are usually written on the left-hand margin of the page beside the appropriate section of dialogue. The sound operator will have cues where sound effects must be introduced, which will have been practised during rehearsals.

HAPPENINGS AT SWIZZLEW

SCRIPT

Scene 4 -- At the Haunted Country House

Henry   What a grand morning for a s;
               shooting, eh what?

Gertrude   A bit too cold for me. I woul
               more winter woolies if I'd kn
               going to drag me off into the

Lucy   Please, come quick! I've just
               on the landing.

Henry   Must be the ghost of old Sir
               regularly walks the corridors
               Hall.

erald   Good grief, old chap. I'd neve
               I'd known.

rtrude   First grouse shooting, now a g
               next? I think I'd almost rathe
               shooting. Come on, Henry. Let'
               Next time you suggest a weekend
               just remember how dry and uneve
               Fulham, will you darling? Now,
               wretched wellies? Have you seen

               No, I haven't dearest.

               Is no-one going to deal with th
               on the landing. I can't possibl

1: If the video director is also the play's director, he must acquire a wide range of skills. Directing actors involves encouraging them to explore their parts for themselves, and helping to shape their performances and isolate those aspects which are most successful. The director must also be sensitive to the relationships between characters on stage, and their movements and body language. However, it is all too easy to get carried away with this aspect of direction, leaving the technical aspects of the production to other members of the team.

Right: Rough sketches of the actors' positions in each scene are useful for planning the shots you wish to get. In performance, the actors will have their positions marked on stage.

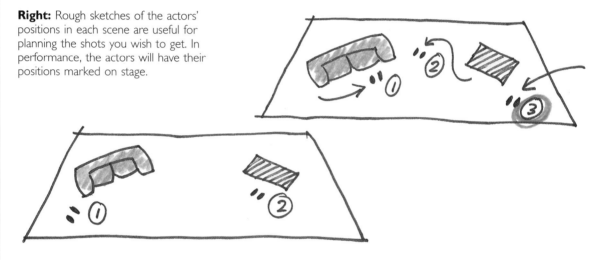

Using Rehearsals

Make as much use of rehearsal time as you can, since there will never seem to be enough of it. The first rehearsal will be a complete read-through of the text which should be attended by the entire video crew – director, and camera, sound and lighting operators. This will enable you and your team to begin visualizing the production, the best possible ways of filming it, and how each member can contribute.

Later, at the early rehearsals, the actors will begin to develop their characters and establish their stage movements. As director, you must now consider the piece in video terms, always having to work round the theatrical production.

Remember that even if you are also the play's director, you cannot alter matters too much or the cast will be unsure whether it is acting for the audience or the lens. However, when filming at a special dress rehearsal which has been set up for the camera you can take certain liberties. The most appropriate involves breaking down the drama into convenient 'takes' (which is standard practice in films). Each scene is rehearsed, after which the sound and lighting are set up. Then the scene is repeated and recorded. If anything goes wrong, or the video director is unhappy with the performance, retakes are possible.

Quite often, scenes are shot out of the order in which they appear in the play when all the relevant characters are already assembled, and the appropriate scenery is in place. But whilst professional actors and actresses may be used to this way of working, amateurs may well find it hard to adapt. Using the take method of working, there is no need to arrange moves in advance. But if a continuous performance is to be recorded, you must have first thought carefully about each scene, determining the best positions for your cameras. And while doing so, ensure that characters will not be obscuring each other.

2–3: During the rehearsals, the actors will be in their everyday dress. If you are going to use the subsequent dress rehearsal **(3)** to get close-up shots for inserts in the final tape, you can use this early period to plan your camera positions. And this means knowing exactly what camera positions you will be using for the full performances, since an insert shot won't work if it is taken from an opposing angle to that used for the major sections of the tape.

4: Another vital consideration is the appearance of groups on stage. Whilst you don't want the actors to have their backs to the camera, you don't want too many head-on shots either. Since the video camera will be recording from the position of the live audience, it is important to adjust the actors' positions for the performance. Such problems should be spotted during the rehearsals.

6: The use of close-ups should be treated with care. A close-up will work well if one of the actors is delivering a monologue alone on stage. But when other characters are present, a close-up of one person alone will prevent you from showing the reactions of others, an equally important part of the performance.

5: In a theatre, the lighting priority is for the stage effect, for what the audience will see. During rehearsals, check that from the camera positions you have chosen, no member of the cast accidentally falls into an area of deep shadow. If so, the remedy may be moving one of the props or modifying the scene to suit your needs.

1–2: When filming a rehearsal, look around the theatre and capture any action in front of the stage. Shots of figures, like the solitary actor learning his lines or the director concentrating on the play, may seem static, but they can provide interludes that will enable you to vary the pace of the video.

3: Mid-shots and close-ups of actors discussing their lines and listening to the director are vital in rehearsal coverage. They show the relationship between the director and the cast, and provide insights into how the production is put together.

4: This shot of the scene-painter at work was one of a sequence showing the backdrop – different parts still at different stages of completion.

5–6: In the lighting gallery there is a wealth of interesting action to cover. But conditions are likely to be cramped, so you will have to take your position carefully – don't get in anyone's way!

7–9 As the actors make up for the dress rehearsal you should be on the alert to capture telling close-ups and long-shots as they exchange nervous jokes.

In Production

'It'll be all right on the night' could just as well be the optimistic battle cry of the video director about to shoot the real performance. You've thought of everything during rehearsals, so it should now, hopefully, be just a matter of letting the cameras 'roll'.

However, it is wiser to take a pessimistic view and plan for the worst. Before filming go through every conceivable check. Ensure that the equipment is in perfect working order and that the electrical connections are sound. Give the cables a good, though not too enthusiastic, tug to ensure that they are firm in their housings. If you are using batteries to power the camcorders, make sure that they are fully charged and that you have spares ready to hand. Double-check the camera positions and the tripod mountings.

And finally, before the production begins, carry out a 15-minute test recording, reviewing it on a monitor to check that the camera is working properly. (Don't use this test tape for the actual recording, since although you can record over the test, quality might be impaired.)

For the first performance, the sound operator will have to double-check sound levels because the acoustics in a full theatre will be very different from those in an empty one. You should also record the expectant hum of the audience in those moments before the curtain opens. This serves as a good introduction for the video, builds tension and, as the noise subsides, signals that the action is about to begin.

When the action does begin, the director should keep in touch with the camera operators. This does not mean hovering behind their backs all the time. They will have their camera moves marked on their scripts and will have rehearsed their shots. The director's purpose is simply to reassure or to help out in emergencies.

After the performance is over, the temptation is immediately to review the material you have shot. But don't. The end of a performance is a time for releasing the tensions that have built up over the past few days or weeks. In any event you will be too close to the material to look at it objectively. Pack the equipment and wait until the next morning before evaluating what you have shot. If you can bear to wait for longer then do so. After two or three days you will approach the piece far more objectively, seeing the film as your intended audience might, instead of watching the version fixed in your imagination.

1: During the first performance, one camera was positioned in the balcony to the left of the stage. This view is very theatrical, which is no bad thing in this context. Since the camera has a wide angle of view, slow pans to follow the action were possible, and do not appear too obtrusive to the viewer.

2–3: Keep the main characters in the centre and do not move the camera too much. Do not worry if the shot is temporarily unbalanced.

4: Only small movements of the camera are necessary to highlight the character who is speaking. By placing him in the centre of the frame, the audience will instinctively direct its attention to him, rather than to the others in the shot.

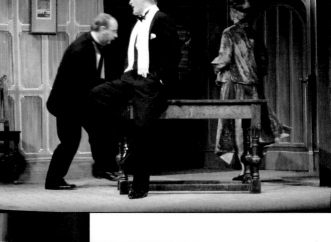

5–6: Track the actress unobtrusively as she comes down the stairs, pulling out slightly to end with both characters in long-shot.

Drama Checklist

Title . . . .

Company . . . .

Venue . . . .

REHEARSAL COVERAGE

PRELIMINARY REHEARSAL
Date   Time   Details of Coverage

_____   _____   _____

_____   _____   _____

_____   _____   _____

TECHNICAL REHEARSAL
Date   Time   Details of Coverage

_____   _____   _____

_____   _____   _____

_____   _____   _____

DRESS REHEARSAL
Date   Time   Details of Coverage

_____   _____   _____

_____   _____   _____

_____   _____   _____

PRODUCTION RUN
Date   Time   Details of Coverage

_____   _____   _____

_____   _____   _____

_____   _____   _____

OTHER SUBJECTS FOR COVERAGE

BACKGROUND TO PRODUCTION
Date   Time   Details of Coverage

_____   _____   _____

_____   _____   _____

_____   _____   _____

SOUND, MUSIC AND LIGHTING

Date	Time	Details of Coverage
_____	_____	_____
_____	_____	_____
_____	_____	_____

MAKE-UP AND COSTUMES

Date	Time	Details of Coverage
_____	_____	_____
_____	_____	_____
_____	_____	_____

MISCELLANEOUS

Date	Time	Details of Coverage
_____	_____	_____
_____	_____	_____

VENUE DATA

POWER SUPPLY ....

LIGHTING REQUIREMENTS ....

SOUND REQUIREMENTS ....

TELEPHONE NUMBERS

VENUE ....

DIRECTOR ....

EQUIPMENT REQUIREMENTS

☐ CAMCORDER AND ACCESSORIES ....

☐ LIGHTS ....

☐ BATTERIES ....

☐ TAPES ....

PEOPLE

DIRECTOR ....

STAGE MANAGER ....

LIGHTING ....

SOUND ....

DESIGNER ....

CAST ....

FRONT OF HOUSE ....

VENUE ADMINISTRATOR ....

A Story Within a Story

A video of a theatrical production can be much more than a simple record of the actors on the stage with a few rehearsal sequences added for extra interest. The whole story of how the play is put together and the relationship between the different people involved can make a fascinating subject in its own right.

To achieve this type of coverage you will, of course, need the full cooperation of all the people involved – you will be filming them off-stage as much as on-stage – and you will have to be discreet. One of the most rewarding areas will be recording the activity backstage. Although you may not be welcome backstage during the run of the production, you will probably be able to film at the dress rehearsal – in fact your presence may help to release tension and dispel nerves.

Before you begin, decide what your approach is going to be – is it the characters of the actors that most interest you, or the mechanics of the production itself?

The shots on this page come from sequences showing the actors applying their make-up. Video is an ideal medium with which to explore this area – the gradual transformation of the actor's face can be shown much better than in stills photography. But there are pitfalls. Beware of uneven lighting – the light is likely to be good around the mirrors, but poor elsewhere, so you may have trouble judging the exposure in long-shots.

1–4: The actor or actress making up is a fascinating subject, but it is usually necessary to inject movement into the sequence by using different camera positions. It may help if the subject's concentration is broken occasionally, as in (**3**), in which she pauses to glance at the camera.

5: The transformation is complete. This head-on shot shows us the finished effect as the actress leaves the dressing room.

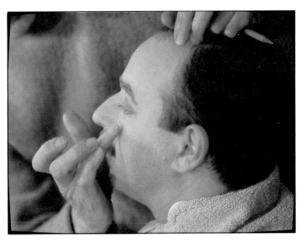

6–8: Close-ups can be an ideal way of showing the viewer exactly what is going on. Again, the subject is static, so it helps if the camera position changes. More apparent movement can be obtained by changing the focus from the subject to his mirror image.

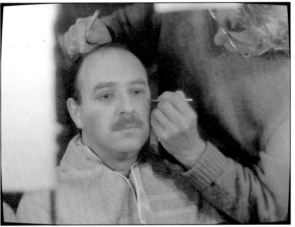

9: Longer shots relieve the intensity of the close-ups – and give an impression of the atmosphere and clutter of the dressing room.

Lighting and Sound Plan

LIGHTING

Production ....

Date ....

	POSITION ON GRID	BAR ONE	BAR TWO	BAR THREE	STANDS
	LANTERN NUMBER				
	CIRCUIT				
	TYPE NUMBER				
	COLOUR				
	SETTING/FOCUS				

CUE	PAGE NO.	WORD CUE	DESCRIPTION	TIME				

SOUND

Production . . . .

Date . . . .

CUE	PAGE NUMBER	EFFECT	TAPE	VOLUME	SPEAKERS

Project Notebook

THEATRE

The possibilities for effective coverage expand with additional equipment and extra crew. But so do your responsibilities. You are using the time and talents of a number of people to achieve your results. Acting the 'director' in the tough, Hollywood mould is going to get you nowhere. The right approach combines co-operation, consultation and courtesy. You should master the art of delegation too. If you entrust someone with the sound, let them get on with it. Your job is to plan and co-ordinate the coverage and to decide exactly which shots you want.

■ Take an overall view of the project, but don't forget to think about the details.

■ Choose a method of working, explain it to your team, and then stick to it. If you suddenly decide to change your mind, explain to everyone exactly why you have done so.

■ Don't replicate material unnecessarily. This sounds obvious, but it is easy, when, say, taking a second shoot, to leave a camera in the same position as it was in the first – from which you already have perfect coverage. The new material that you get from a new position might not be of any use, but, on the other hand, it just might be.

■ When working with a limited team, make sure that each person is capable of carrying out the roles you have allocated. Remember, no-one can check for continuity lapses and monitor sound levels at the same time. Give them compatible roles.

■ Think of the others. *You* might be ready and eager to go for the twenty-second take of a scene. The actors might appreciate a lunch break.

■ Make clear at the outset what rewards your helpers will get – an end-of-shoot meal, perhaps, or an invitation to a party for the first showing of the tape. Everyone works better with some treat in store, no matter how small.

Editing Techniques

The question of editing has been touched upon at various stages in this book. This chapter looks at editing and other post-production options in detail. It examines editing procedures and the different styles of editing that can be used to shape your coverage into a polished, finished tape. Many of these techniques can be achieved at home, but to achieve stable, professional-looking tapes may require the use of more professional studio equipment. Sophisticated electronic special effects, familiar to everyone through the explosion of pop videos, may be expensive, but the chapter also offers alternatives available to the amateur.

Shooting to Edit

Rock videos borrow from all other video disciplines, using elements of drama, fantasy, documentary and action coverage. The intention is to produce a tape which conveys an 'image' of the band and matches its kind of music.

Before editing, however, you have to make several basic decisions. For example, will you be using a studio tape for the sound track (as is likely), so that sound recordings on location become redundant? (The only exception to this circumstance would be when recording a live performance, for which professional sound engineers would be essential.) Also, when scripting the video (which will probably be done in co-operation with the band) you will have to decide what is, and what is not possible in terms of video technique and the resources available.

Once such matters have been tackled, you must then consider your coverage in detail. If you can shoot with two or more cameras so much the better. If not, ask the band to perform a number of times to get shots from as many different angles as possible. A pre-shoot location check will be necessary to ensure that you have unusual backgrounds and camera positions.

In a rock video, the editing conventions that would apply, for instance, to a drama, are far less important. For example, you can jump from one shot to another, changing camera angles and frame sizes between cuts in a way that would be incoherent in conventional work. In fact, the main dangers are that your coverage will be too static and that there will not be enough variety of material with which to edit.

Don't be afraid to try the seemingly preposterous – you can always discard it later when edit-

ing. The musicians will probably prefer an original approach in their video rather than something that has been done a thousand times before.

Using locations

A rock video allows you to be bold with locations. In recent years particular styles have been established by professional producers. The two styles that stand out are the exotic tropical beach and the backstreet city scene. Factory interiors, run-down and derelict sites, docklands and underground car parks are other alternatives.

When drawing up rough storyboard ideas for the rock video, keep the band's music in mind. A heavy metal group is not going to be too keen on an idyllic rural setting. Listen to the lyrics of the song to discover if there are any references you can illustrate visually, or which can become the basis of your narrative. And finally ensure that your video ideas match the image that the band members have of themselves.

Below: When you plan a rock video don't get so carried away by the images that you forget the music itself. Keep listening to a tape of the song and refer to the lyrics.

Power of Editing

Editing is at the heart of the video-making process. At the most basic level, its purpose is to eliminate poor shots and other mistakes, ensuring that your audience sees a slick, polished video. But in most cases, the value of editing is far greater than this. Extensive editing means imparting a sense of pace and rhythm to a tape.

In the case of a rock video this is a particularly important consideration. The images must match the soundtrack for pace and excitement. In professional rock videos, therefore, cuts between shots

The shots on this page show the raw material available when editing a rock tape. The coverage shows the group playing inside a power plant. Being an unusual backdrop it provokes interest. And there is also a deliberate link between the potentially explosive nature of energy and the group's music.

tend to be rapid and obtrusive, with the video director drawing the audience's attention to his or her techniques. With quieter, more melodic soundtracks, the reverse is the case – cuts should be unobtrusive and serve only to allow the story to unfold clearly.

Editing can also have a profound effect on the meaning conveyed by the images. Consider, for example, a sequence showing a group of youths walking down a street and another showing a senior citizen out shopping. By rapidly cutting between each one, you could easily create a sense of menace, implying that the youths were about to attack the senior citizen. If instead the two sequences are shown consecutively, there is no menace, just street scenes. The power of editing to manipulate how a viewer interprets visual information should never be underestimated.

On the other hand, there need not necessarily be a sense of menace when using these two elements, so much as a sense of identity. By clever intercutting you could suggest that one day these youths will resemble the senior citizen – or that the senior citizen would like to relive his own youth. You could make any one of these suggestions using the same basic material just by editing it differently. But in a rock video these techniques will have to reflect the words of the song – then their effect will be even more powerful.

Another possibility is to make the images reflect the music in a more abstract way, responding to the changes in rhythm, pitch and dynamics rather like disco lights. In this case it would matter less what the actual subject matter of the video was. It would be much more important to make the edits so that they synchronize exactly with the music. This sort of technique could produce a rather relentless result if used all the way through a

1: Sequence showing the band approaching the camera along one of the long interior corridors. Could use as a repeated cut on the beat of the song. Make sure band recognizable when it is at far end of corridor.

2: Check this sequence for any interference caused by the fluorescent lighting. White balance system seems to have worked adequately. Watch out for distortion of verticals caused by camera angle.

3: This end-of-sequence shot looks a bit too posed. Like shot 1, it could be used as a repeated cut, but only for very short bursts – probably better to stick to earlier shots from the sequence.

4: Don't like the framing in this – it seems confused and no one is really prominent. Movement is too horizontal across frame – no diagonals. Not exactly a disaster, but we would prefer to drop it.

video. But employed in a short, dynamic sequence it can be very effective, forcibly drawing the viewer's attention to the patterns in the music.

At the end of the day, the way you edit a rock video should depend on the effect that the musicians want, and there are as many ways of editing as there are of making music. Listen as much as you can to the track you are making the video for and some influence is bound to rub off.

Finally, remember that, although the musicians will probably demand to have the final choice, you can make as many different suggestions to them as you like. They will not necessarily know about every effect that you can create in video, and there is a world of difference between a romantic, Hollywood-inspired approach and a staccato, post-modernist one. You should be aware of as many different alternatives in editing methods and approaches as possible.

5: OK, but a bit contrived. The main problem really is that this sequence is a bit too friendly – it doesn't convey the high-tech, hard-edged atmosphere we are looking for. Suggest that we cut it out.

6: A useful shot. The low camera angle which not only emphasizes the size of the building but it also gives a good frame for the singer. The background is not too confusing but it is still really not hi-tech enough.

7: Again, this has the background we are looking for, and continues nicely where the crab-shot leaves off (see below). Definitely use this footage, although this will be used later in the final video.

8: Good, strong performance coverage. Watch out that the two performers at back are not obscured for too long as camera crabs round. Can use provided that we also keep wide-angle shot showing all of band.

9: Zoom in from the preceding long-shot of whole band. A good close-up to cut in during the guitar riff. This could have been shot on a separate occasion for use during this instrumental part of the song.

The Medium

Video editing is an electronic process. It involves copying the magnetic patterns from one tape to another. This is done by playing the original tape in one video machine (often the camcorder), and connecting this to another video machine (usually a VCR) which records the electronic signals via a set of leads. The set-up for this process is described in the section on Basic Video Editing on pages 54–55.

There is one main disadvantage with editing video tape that is not present when handling film. As film is physically cut, you can add new shots to your film wherever you so desire. You add a new section and the rest just gets shunted along. This is not possible with video tape. Anything you add either has to be placed at the end of what you have recorded already, or it has to physically replace something that is already there. Careful planning is therefore necessary. Imagine that you spend hours carefully editing your video, only to find out that you need to add a title sequence to the beginning. If there is no space left for this, you may have to start the whole copying process again.

The generation game

A solution in this situation could be to copy your edited version onto a third tape – leaving enough room for your new opening section. However, this presents a problem. Each time a tape is copied, the quality of the copy is slightly worse than the original. If we make a copy of the copy of the original (which is known as a third-generation recording) there is a risk that the quality will be unacceptable. Noise levels in the picture and soundtrack will have increased, and colours will deteriorate. What's worse, the control tracks will have also deteriorated. These control tracks provide the sync signals that ensure that the heads of the video recorder can find the beginnings of each of the diagonal video tracks correctly. If these signals are very deteriorated vertical lines in the video picture can appear as diagonals!

In practice, therefore, we try to edit videos so that the final version (called the edit master) is only a second-generation recording (a copy of the first-generation original tape). Again, this means very careful planning to ensure that we get each section of film in the right place. It is also the reason that serious video makers use high-band tape formats (Hi8, S-VHS and S-VHS-C). This ensures that we start off with the best-quality picture possible, so that any deterioration when copying will still leave us an acceptably good picture. This is especially important if you are making copies of your edited videos to give (or sell) to others – as these will have to be third-generation recordings.

Choosing the top grades of video tape at each stage is another way in which we can help to minimize the loss of quality. The better the tape, the better the original recording, or the more accurately it can record from the source tape. Compared with the amount of time you can waste at the editing stage, even top-priced tapes are cheap.

One advantage that video has is that it is possible to record over it time and time again. So in editing, you record a section at a time, and then check that you have recorded the exact piece you require. If the section starts at slightly the wrong point, you can then re-record this scene then and there.

Edit VCRs

When editing, it is especially important to be able to find the exact point on both source and record tapes where a particular scene begins or ends. For this reason enthusiasts will use special VCRs which have fine transport controls. For example, a typical edit-grade VCR will have a jog/shuttle dial. This has two concentric dials. The outer one (the shuttle dial) will give fast forward and rewind control at progressive speed the more you turn it. The inner jog dial is the fine control, allowing you to progress through the tape a single frame at a time. VCRs of this kind are also available in the S-VHS, 8mm and Hi8 formats.

The source and record machines can be controlled manually without any other equipment. However, being able to synchronize the two machines so that you record the exact scene you want requires a high degree of manual dexterity.

With practice, this manual method is fine for simple editing where you have only a few scenes to rearrange. But with more complex edits, involving maybe, hundreds of scenes such as in our rock video, you need some automatic help. This is where the edit controller comes in. It memorizes the in and out points that you pinpoint as you watch the original tape, and then copies them all across slavishly when you say so. It will synchronize the start of the two machines, allowing for backspace editing, in a far more consistent way than you can ever hope to achieve manually. What's more a good edit controller gives you a read-out of these in/out points, called an edit decision list. You can then move scenes around, and alter their lengths to get the result you want.

Right: The diagram shows the degeneration of the video image as successive copies of a tape are made. The degeneration is more likely to occur in a heavily edited tape, since this will have more inherent electronic instability.

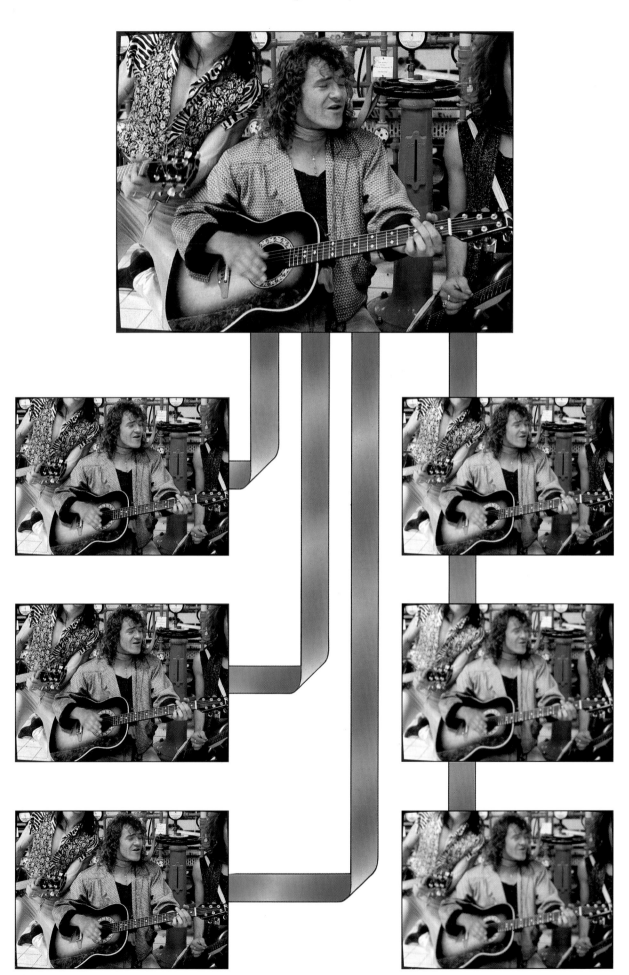

Professional Equipment

In professional video, the budget may allocate as much money for the post-production stage as for the actual shoot. The complex computer-based editing equipment found in top professional edit suites is very expensive indeed. Hire rates can be calculated in terms of thousands of pounds per hour. However, there are opportunities for the amateur to use similar equipment. Local colleges and arts centres may also have basic professional facilities available for hire at a modest fee – and certainly a lot cheaper than buying your own edit equipment.

If you do obtain access to such facilities, precisely what equipment might you use, and what advantages will such equipment bring? Knowing this in advance will enable you to be more ambitious when planning your own project.

The most sophisticated editing suites resemble the mission control rooms for space shuttle flights. The computer power available is not much less. Here, images can be manipulated at will to create a huge range of special effects. And there is still the basic editing equipment to perform the fundamental editing process of arranging cuts in the required sequences.

The editing suite consists of a panel of in-built monitors and a huge array of controls. Many of these controls have solely technical functions, regulating the transport and playback of the tape on source and edit decks. Others control the audio signal, allowing levels to be adjusted. Those which control the image alone allow varying degrees of adjustment – colour tone, brightness and contrast, for example, or speed, so that fast or slow motion sequences can be introduced.

There may also be the option of a wide variety of special effects – wipes, tumbles, dissolves and other transitions for you to use between scenes. In most studios there will be a technician who will be thoroughly skilled in using the facility and who will work to your instructions, so you should not worry overmuch about precise technicalities.

Right: A computer-controlled professional edit suite provides the full facilities for mixing video and audio material. A skilled editor will operate the suite and help you obtain the effects you require.

If you do get into an editing suite remember that time is money, big money. You should therefore arrive well prepared knowing exactly what you want to achieve. This is not the time to be indecisive, wondering, perhaps, whether another idea would be more appropriate. A good tip is to do a rough edit using your equipment at home. The pros call this an off-line edit. You basically decide which scenes you want, and copy them across. You are not worried about supreme accuracy – you just want to have an idea of what works before you do the final 'on-line' edit in the suite.

Take along your clearly labelled master material (the original tapes) and an editing script with each cut marked and timed. The script should also indicate on which of the master tapes the material is located, and exactly where it is on that tape. Before getting down to work, you will be able to go over material with the studio editor.

Once the editing begins, the editor will inform you of any problems that occur. Perhaps a required cut that you wish to make is not possible at the exact point indicated because you neglected to allow enough editing margin on the shot.

(When shooting, remember to set the camera rolling five seconds before action begins.) After each cut, the editor will replay it so that you can check that you have the footage you want and that the edit is stable.

A good suite will also have a timebase corrector. This unassuming black box has the ability to replace worn sync signals, helping to eliminate some of the quality-loss problems associated with multi-generation copies.

While making the edit, the editor will be continuously checking audio and video levels and looking for signs of instability in the image. He or she may point out small glitches that had escaped you when you reviewed the material. Also, he or she will be available to answer any questions you might have.

The edit controller here is likely to be of the 'A/B roll' variety – allowing you to control two source decks simultaneously. This is of particular benefit when using a vision mixer, so that you can dissolve between two different video pictures, on different tapes, instead of always performing straight cuts between your sequences.

1–2: A review of sequences taken by a tank of acid was logged, even though on first sight the material did not look promising. The sequences were taken early on in the shoot when the band appeared too static. Why not incorporate the shots of the lead singer lying down as a flash insert?

3–4: The band performed a number of times in different locations, both inside and outside the power station. Material that seems superficially similar should be clearly described on the log sheet, so that you can quickly find the shot that you want. Also, note who is in shot for each sequence.

5–6: Some of the coverage was tried from unusual angles. This bird's eye view taken from a gantry high above the group gave a good sense of the location used. As it is easy to ignore background when shooting, it is worth taking a few shots in which it is prominent for use when editing.

Analyzing the Coverage

At the end of the shoot you will have a number of tapes containing different areas of coverage. These tapes are your masters, the ones from which you will eventually create the final high-quality edit.

The first step is to make copies of these tapes (known by many professionals as 'dubs') to work with during the rough editing stage – to save wear on the originals. At this point it is best to dub all of the material on the master tapes, even if you feel sure that some of it is unusable – you may find you do want to use it, after all.

The next step is to review all the coverage and write down the scenes on a logging sheet. Each should be given a brief description, plus the time counter reading at the beginning and end of each shot taken from the tape. Also, indicate if some of the shots are poor, or don't work in any way. This log sheet will be the basis from which you will develop a full editing script.

Logging is a laborious process, but repays the effort. Review the dubs a number of times, so that you are absolutely familiar with your material

(always remember to reset the tape counter on the machine to zero each time you replay the tapes). And when stopping the tape to enter a description on the log sheet, put the machine into a full stop, since the pause mode can wear both the tapes and the machine's video heads unnecessarily.

With the rock video, the music acts as the lead to the script. Naturally, you will want to follow the music in terms of pace and also tie the visuals in to the sound track so that the guitar solo music shows the lead guitarist and not the drummer! A brief timed breakdown of the soundtrack is therefore useful for matching with the times of sequences recorded in the logged dubs.

The task now is to select sequences and images that will match the pace of the soundtrack and also offer visual variety and excitement. From the log sheet you will probably be able to select these in rough outline and begin the fist rough cut of the final tape. It doesn't matter if at this stage the images are not in synchronization with the sound – the fine tuning can come later.

7–8: This mid-shot of the guitarist was filmed two different ways. First from a low-angle, and then from the same position with a Dutch tilt. Which shot do you think looks the most striking?

9: Since the power station was located close to the coast, beach scenes were also taken for variety. Although the weather was grey and overcast, the situation was salvaged by using special-effects filters, so making the shots deliberately unnaturalistic. In fact, the coverage obtained using the filters was an improvement on the original idea.

10: When examining the material you have obtained, you often discover shots that you didn't realize you'd taken. This composition of the singer's head framed by two large valve-ends is a case in point. At the time the shot was just another close-up of an individual band member in a different location. It was only afterwards that it became obvious that a striking image had been filmed that had to be included.

11–12: Two-colour filters of different strengths provided simple special effects.

Editing Considerations

When you begin editing a piece of work, you must have a clear idea of your intentions. With the rock video, these are obvious: to create an exciting blend of sound and image that successfully conveys the group's music and personality. But in other areas of video the intentions may be more complex. In a documentary, for example, you may wish to edit your material in such a way that a particular argument is strengthened. In a drama, your first priority will be to ensure that the narrative is clearly presented and that cuts from one scene to another do not confuse the viewer, but you may also decide to emphasize the dramatic or the comic in your coverage.

For the rock video, the choices were narrowed down. The material consisted of the band in a series of different locations. There were also shots of individual band members, some taken using effects filters. Finally, there was a great deal of material showing the band performing, taken from a range of angles and using a variety of different shots, from extreme long-shot to extreme close-up. The editing problem, once the unsatisfactory shots had been weeded out, involved assembling this material to create a fast-moving video. In fact, once the major sequences had been chosen, the creation of the actual edit was largely a matter of trial and error, using the dub tapes.

1–3: When reviewing the material in the log sheet, it was decided to place sequences of the group on the beach, and those filmed using colour filters, one after the other for a dramatic effect. The effect was further heightened by beginning the sequence using the filtered shot, cutting briefly to the natural scene and then resuming with the filtered material. When making the cut, it is important to achieve a similarity between the two shots, in terms of camera position and camera angle.

1–2: Notice the position of the horizon in the two filter shots. When using half filters, the effect is diminished if the coloured areas move around too much on the screen. This is particularly important when making cuts – a sudden jump in coloured areas will appear obtrusive on the screen.

4–5: Don't rely totally on rapid changes of shot to give pace and rhythm to the edited tape. Some of the coverage should have included moving camera shots which can be used in short sequences. These shots come from a track in, taken on one of the outdoor locations on the shoot.

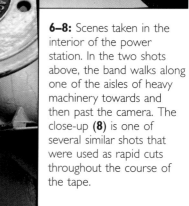

6–8: Scenes taken in the interior of the power station. In the two shots above, the band walks along one of the aisles of heavy machinery towards and then past the camera. The close-up **(8)** is one of several similar shots that were used as rapid cuts throughout the course of the tape.

Editing Sound

The sound track is critical in a rock video. This sound will be recorded separately in a studio, and could simply be audio dubbed onto the mono track of the video tape at the editing stage. You may not even need a sound mixer as you will not need to adjust levels; this will have been done in the studio. Before you do this the tape must be 'blacked'. This means recording a black picture along the entire tape (or as much of it that you will use). You can record this with your camcorder directly connected to the VCR with its lens cap on. Set the VCR to record from its AV input and away you go. Having done this and having made your audio dub, you can then insert edit all the pictures as and where you want them.

Suppose, however, that you intend to make a video about the group: its history and the views of its members as well as their music. This means you will have to deal with three types of sound in the edit: studio recording, location sound, and a voice-over or commentary. Each of these sound sources will have a different level and quality.

Editing the sound track means establishing a uniformity, for a sudden drop or rise in sound levels sounds bad. Assuming that you are using a basic arrangement of source and edit decks and an edit controller, you will be able to adjust sound in a limited way.

The first necessity is to rehearse the edit and listen to the sound on headphones, whilst watching the levels on the volume unit meter on the edit deck. Rely on what the VU meter tells you rather than on the evidence of your ears. You should adjust the level using the manual level control on the edit deck, not the source deck. Play back to the beginning of the cut, and then make the edit,

1–3: If you are going to record sound on location, you will have a few major problems using relatively sophisticated equipment. Note however that the sound environments of these three locations differ greatly. Yet with the use of a graphic equalizer, the three sound signals can be modified so that they could be used in the final edit.

adjusting the levels to those established in the rehearsal. Review the edit, and make a note of the levels shown on the VU meter (they will always be slightly different to those you rehearsed). The levels on this edit are those to match on each succeeding cut, and this will be the case no matter what the sound source.

You will probably lay the sound track down on the first rough edit. Remember that once you do that any sound on the original audio track will be lost. Check for obvious discrepancies: for example, don't have extended close-ups of one particular instrument when another is dominating the sound track.

The level of control you will have over your sound track depends very much on the kind of equipment you are using. Fortunately, the march of miniaturization has extended even into audio equipment, bringing increased sophistication and lower prices. Quite sophisticated multi-track recording units, synthesizers and sequencers are now available for a few hundred pounds which allow considerable adjustment of the sound signal, offering, for example, reverb, repeat and echo effects. With this equipment, you can edit the sound track independently before dubbing it onto the video tape. Most musicians will either have such facilities or know someone who has.

On a straightforward dub to video, the procedure is relatively simple. Sound can be heard through headphones or through the output of a monitor if a microphone input is not being used. When working with multiple sound sources, remember that deterioration also occurs with audio tape, so use dub sound for rough cut stages, preserving the original material as masters.

You will find more information about sound editing, including instructions for a simple sound-edit using a multi-track tape recorder, in the section on Sound Editing (pages 56–57).

4: On the final video, pictures and sound will not only have to be synchronized, but you'll need to match close-ups to solo performances.

Music on Video

The sport of ballooning is not only physically challenging but also visually exciting. We wanted to reflect this by making a 'musical' video, and we began by going for colourful close-ups of the preparation of the balloon for its flight. One of the shots pulls in gradually from out-of-focus, revealing a mysterious pattern of yellow and red – it is a balloon envelope before inflation. At the editing stage, we decided to begin the video with this shot, and then to go on as planned to show the process of getting the balloon airborne.

Although the shots were covered with good location sound recorded in synchronization with the pictures (the roar of the gas burner and the voices of the crew) we needed something extra to heighten the feeling of mystery and adventure, so music was used as a major element of the sound track. We aimed to weave it into the video at appropriate points, which had the additional advantage of strengthening the continuity of the piece – there was no spoken commentary to play this role. Atmospheric music would reflect both the sense of expectation before take-off and the soaring of the balloon as it made its way across the sky.

The sound track was built up on a separate multi-track tape recorder that was electronically sync-locked to the video pictures. This was a specially adapted machine with mixing facilities, which allowed us to build up the sound track in stages before laying it back onto the video tape.

When the shots had been assemble-edited onto a copy video tape, the location sound was transferred onto one track of the sound tape. The mood music was then dubbed at the right points on a parallel track, and additional spot effects were either dubbed into the spaces on the second track or recorded onto a third track. The roar of the gas burner, for example, was not quite strong enough on the original location video sound track, and so was reinforced with a spot effect that had been recorded on a cassette machine.

The premixed effects track and the music tracks were recorded at full level to maximize sound quality and, when completed, they were then dubbed onto the video tape via a sound mixer. During this process, the levels were adjusted to fade the music in and out of the natural sound. It is possible to do this redubbing operation in stages, but it is best to do it as a single non-stop process. You will find this hard at first, but with practice you will be able to keep up with the flow.

1: The video begins with the puzzling image of red and yellow stripes. The camera slowly pans over these and the focus is pulled so that the true nature of the subject is gradually revealed. Music on the sound track sets the mood.

2–3: The rippling of the fabric as the envelope starts to inflate is complemented by slow camera pans and the music rippling along on the sound track. As the inflation of the balloon continues, the horizontal stripes turn to verticals and the music shifts up in mood to match this.

4: A human element is introduced, helping us to see what is happening more clearly. Location sound is faded in, but the music is still the dominant element on the sound track.

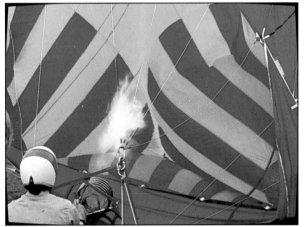

5: A cut to a close-up of the balloon interior seen from its underside heightens the drama, and the taut fabric now makes a bold pattern. On the sound track the noise of the burner increases, and the music drops back further in level.

6: At the cut back to a closer view of the crew and burner, the location sound takes over completely.

7–8: This tilt shot give us our first views of the balloon exterior. We can still hear the noise of the burner, but the other sounds at the location become increasingly audible. The music is faded out completely.

9: With take-off, a completely different mood takes over. First there is the feeling of triumph at the lift-off, then an atmosphere of peace takes over as the balloon travels further away from the ground. The music returns and gradually swells to dominate the sound track, with the voices of the spectators on the ground barely audible.

Voice-Over

At the ballooning event described on the previous two pages, a second production team was also present to shoot material for a video with a very different approach. The intention of this second crew was to make a straight documentary which would be shown mainly to enthusiasts of the sport; there was also the possibility that the video might be used commercially by one or more of the balloon sponsors.

The team had the services of a keen balloonist who advised them on which aspects of the sport to cover, so that the video was technically complete and authoritative – a must when there is a potential audience of experts and enthusiasts. This consultant also helped with the scripting of the commentary at a later stage in the production.

So, instead of the dominant music on the first video, the sound track was limited mainly to the sound of the commentator, with some background sound. The latter was mostly made up of long-running sound effects which were recorded onto separate sound tapes at the event; this allowed the team to avoid intrusive cuts in the sound when making picture edits later, and to use the sound background to bridge over the edits within groups of shots.

But there were a few shots – mainly action close-ups – in which the original location sync-sound was retained. In contrast to the previous video, music had a minor role but it was used to set the all-important mood at the beginning and also to end the video.

The same basic techniques were used as for the 'musical' video, with the addition of commentary recording facilities. The sequence illustrated is a final one, showing the balloons taking to the air.

The video was first edited and the original sync location sound was lifted and transferred onto a sync-locked multi-track sound tape. The separately recorded non-sync background sound was then premixed onto another track of the tape. The shots were timed, the commentary scripted to match, and the voice-over was recorded onto a parallel track of the sound tape.

To ensure that the commentary was covering the correct points at exactly the right time in the video, a playback of the pictures was used to provide the start-cues for each section of the voice-over.

The combined voice-over and background tracks were finally recorded back onto the video tape via an audio mixer to produce the finished mixed sound track.

1–3: These are the opening shots of a sequence showing the take-off of a group of balloons. To satisfy both the enthusiasts and the sponsors, the commentary includes a blend of technical and topical information – including references to the people, the balloons, and who provided the money. The commentary is supplemented by live background sound.

4–6: As the balloons are ready to take off, their sponsors' names are clear. Further shots of individual balloons follow, intercut with wide-shots of the balloon-filled sky. The background sound broadens too, with more ambient sounds and fewer clear details on the sound track.

Rostrum Camera Techniques

Television arts programmes have made us familiar with the close-up of a work of art, in which the camera travels across the canvas picking out particular details. The success of such shots depends upon the stability of the camera, the lighting, and your analysis of the details you wish to show.

To check how close you can go with your lens while maintaining acceptable picture quality, take sample shots and review them on a full-size TV screen (the quality of the image in the camcorder's viewfinder is not good enough for this purpose). You can get really close with the wide-angle setting of the zoom, thanks to its macro mode, but this causes problems with lighting – as the camera casts shadows on what you are trying to video. It is better to use a more telephoto setting, and shoot from its minimum focusing distance.

The camera should be mounted on a tripod. A good tripod head which allows smooth movement is essential. Your analysis should not be too 'bitty', with the camera jumping from one area of the subject to another. Remember that the viewer needs to be able to relate the position of each close-up detail to the whole image, so move in a steady, continuous motion and return to the full frame at the end.

1–2: Move the camera, using a dolly, to pull back from a fixed camcorder position or to give the effect of moving in close.

3–5: Moving the camera slowly across the surface of a painting can actually give the viewer a feeling that the people in the image are themselves in motion. But you should not continue such close-up sequences for too long or the viewer will forget how they relate to the painting as a whole.

6–7: Close-ups can give a good idea of the texture of the paint on the canvas.

8–9: Gradually broadening the angle of view puts the buildings in their context – and gives the viewer a sense of the whole painting.

Special Effects

The amazing range of special effects that characterizes so many professional rock videos used to be achieved only at enormous cost. But now such tricks are possible with some top-of-the-range amateur equipment.

Like everything else in video work, special effects must be planned in the early stages of a project. The simplest effects are achieved in-camera, using filters, gels and mattes, or by using special lighting techniques.

One effect commonly used in all forms of video work, from news broadcasts to science-fiction series is known as colour separation overlay, or, more often, Chromakey, the trade name for the technique. Chromakey relies on electronically removing one particular colour value from the shot – traditionally blue – and then filling in the available space with another scene. For example, actors in a science-fiction film might perform on an all-blue background. But when the blue is removed it can be substituted with a completely different background: suddenly the actors are on the surface of an alien planet! (Of course, care must be taken that no part of the actors' costumes contains blue, since that will also disappear when the background is wiped.)

Picture-in-picture effects are also commonly used. This is the electronic addition of two shots, or parts of two shots. It is commonly used to include the talking head of a foreign correspondent in the top corner of the screen, while the action fills the rest of the area.

Superimposition, wipes and dissolves are carried out using a special-effects generator vision mixer. The equipment receives signals from two or more sources. To achieve a dissolve, one signal is gradually reduced as the other is strengthened. If the two signals are held mid-way, then a double exposure effect is achieved. With a wipe, one image gradually pushes another from the screen.

In recent years, the increasing computerization of editing equipment has meant that the image can now be manipulated in many other ways. Since the video signal is digitized it can be analyzed down to its smallest components: those which dictate every aspect of the image on the screen. The electronics in a computerized edit suite can alter it in any number of ways. The image can appear to be torn in two, crumpled up, or repeated hundreds of times. Colour values can be changed and graphic images can be superimposed on real action.

2: If Chromakey is to be used, it must be taken into account during the shooting stage. This shot illustrates the blue background which is later electronically removed, and a new background substituted.

3–4: The new background is videoed separately and then is cued in electronically behind the performer.

5: A simple special effect involves using a video negative, or reverse video. At the post-production stage, the effect can usually be readily obtainable with many AV processors. The technique simply reverses the colour value of the signal, creating, in effect, the equivalent of a negative in conventional photography.

1: Solarization is a technique achieved in photography by special processing of the film. The same effect can be achieved electronically with a video during the editing stage if reasonably sophisticated special-effects equipment is available in the editing suite.

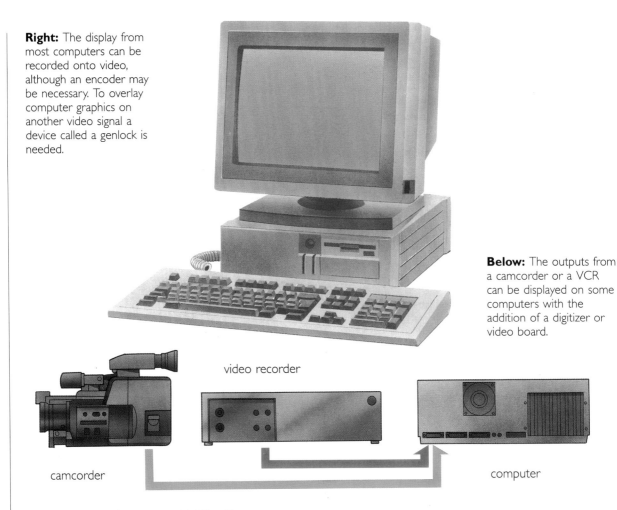

Right: The display from most computers can be recorded onto video, although an encoder may be necessary. To overlay computer graphics on another video signal a device called a genlock is needed.

Below: The outputs from a camcorder or a VCR can be displayed on some computers with the addition of a digitizer or video board.

video recorder

camcorder

computer

Desktop Video

It's only a matter of a few years ago that high-quality graphics were not possible without the most sophisticated computers. Today colour displays with high resolutions are commonplace, and the processing power needed to support graphic design is the norm.

The one problem is that, on most computers, it is not possible to record these graphics directly to a video recorder, because the signals are generally incompatible. To get round this you will probably need a device called an encoder, which will translate the computer's display to something which can be recorded directly on video. If you want to superimpose the output of the computer over your video footage you will, instead, need a genlock. This will allow you to put merge graphics and titles with your movies. Even animated graphics are now possible.

Another exciting possibility is to link your VCR (or camcorder) the other way round – so that you can display video stills, or even live footage, on your computer screen.

This means that you can import images from video tape into your documents, for instance, using a slot-in computer card called a digitizer. DTV (desktop video) is the term that is used to describe such interactions between computer and video. It is a world that is developing so fast that feats that cost thousands one year, are readily available to the amateur the next.

One of the most exciting areas is the use of computers as an all-in-one edit suite. A single computer expansion card can now replace the need for an edit controller, title generator, sound mixer, special-effects generator, vision mixer, and timebase corrector.

At the other end of the scale, simple computer programs are fast taking over from stand-alone edit controllers. Computers are extremely adept at handling the transport mechanisms of suitable camcorders and VCRs, with the addition of a special communication lead, or interface box. The number of edits that are possible are virtually infinite, as the computer's hard drive (or separate disc) can be used to store the edit decision lists. With a suitable video board, the output from your camcorder can even be displayed on your computer as you edit, and snapshots from the in- and output can (in some instances) be recorded by the computer as part of the edit decision list, giving you a visual storyboard representation of the cuts you have made.

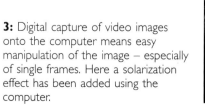

1–2: These images were created by an artist using a powerful computer graphics program. They were achieved by building up the image stage by stage over a series of operations. .

3: Digital capture of video images onto the computer means easy manipulation of the image – especially of single frames. Here a solarization effect has been added using the computer.

Project Notebook

ROCK VIDEO

As pointed out in the Introduction, editing considerations are vital to video. You must shoot your material with editing in mind. This means always checking how you covered the scene the last time you shot before you go for another take. It's not just continuity errors that can cause problems – if you cross the line between two takes you are going to have major headaches when trying to edit the material. For the editing process itself, nothing is more valuable than complete familiarity with the material – exactly what you've got and where it is on the tapes. That's why it is so important to log the tapes before you try to do anything else, no matter what kind of editing set-up you've got at your disposal.

■ Editing is a process of elimination and juxtaposition – eliminating material that is no good or simply redundant, and juxtaposing sequences so that the story unfolds.

■ Editing serves to hone the story you want to tell. You can't do that until you yourself are sure exactly what that story is.

■ Remember that the sound track is just as important as the images. Listen to it with the same attention to detail as you pay to your visual coverage. In a well-edited tape, sound and image have a matching rhythm.

■ Edit to the prospective audience. In an educational tape for children, the information should be given in smaller doses, and more slowly, than in a tape covering a similar subject for adult enthusiasts.

■ The way a piece is edited can radically affect the meaning it conveys on the screen. Check that the way you juxtapose images and sequences does not convey meanings that you never intended.

APPENDICES

Technical Information

The invention of the camcorder has meant that video has extended its reach from the recording of television programmes and the home viewing of movies. It is now a creative medium in its own right. It is also available to everyone, not just as a leisure pursuit, but also as a powerful communication tool.

The rapid growth in video making has been a worldwide phenomenon, which should, theoretically, mean people who are separated by distance can keep in touch with each other with video tapes. The main drawback is that there are invisible barriers which prevent the free international exchange in videos.

One barrier we have already mentioned in this book is the existence of a number of different tape formats which are incompatible with each other. For instance, 8mm cassettes will not replay on VHS machines unless the recording is first copied onto a VHS tape. Commercial pressures and technical advances have meant that we do not have the single tape size.

A world divided

The next barrier to universal tape compatibility is even harder to get around. It is all a matter of the different television standards used by different countries. Suppose you shot a family video and wanted to send it to friends in Australia. Will they be able to play it? The answer will depend on whether the recorder that made the tape used the same television system that they will play it on.

It is largely a matter of history and political wrangling that we have three main television standards in use around the world today. It all dates back to the introduction of colour television back in the 1950s and 60s. The American National Television Standards Committee was the first out of the starting block with a 30-frame-per-second 525-line system. It was called NTSC, after the body that thought it up, and is still widely in use throughout North America, Japan and elsewhere.

Most of Europe and Britain opted for a superior 25-frame-per-second 625-line system called PAL (phase alternation line). The French went their own way with SECAM (séquenciel couleur à mémoire), a derivative of which was used in much of Eastern Europe and the former Soviet Union. A list of countries worldwide and the television systems they use is given in the table overleaf.

Since these introductions were made, the world has therefore been divided. The situation has been made even more complicated by a number of

small variations between these three main standards – each adding incompatibility problems.

Much of the difference between the standards is in the way that the sound and video is broadcast – the way in which they are recorded on tape is more similar. For example, a tape sent from Britain will play perfectly in an Australian video recorder. However, because the Australians use PAL B, whilst Britain uses PAL I, you could not take your television from one country to the other and expect it to work.

Those who want to plug their camcorders into the televisions in a foreign hotel could be disappointed. A tip to increase the chance of success in this situation is to plug the camcorder into the video in socket, rather than using the aerial lead.

For those who want a solution to these problems, there are multi-standard VHS recorders on the market that can play most types of tape. In Europe, many VCRs are capable of playing NTSC tapes with suitable TVs, thanks to a piece of electronic trickery. Unfortunately, the reverse is not the case – NTSC tape decks are not fitted with the ability to play PAL tapes.

Whilst we are talking about the problems of travelling, it might seem that the different electrical voltages used around the globe might also cause a problem. Fortunately nearly all of today's battery-charger and mains adaptors are multi-voltage and can handle anything from 100–250 volts and alternating currents with frequencies from 50–60Hz. You will undoubtedly need a new plug – or that essential companion for the jet-setter, the travel adaptor.

Future developments

One of the inescapable facts about video is the speed in which models change and new, better features appear. Video is a relatively new medium to the world – and camcorders are even younger. In a short time, therefore, the quality of video pictures and sound has developed at an amazing pace. Features to help make video-making easier, or to add more scope for creativity, seem to be introduced every other month.

Whilst these changes are good for the advancement of technology, it does mean that there is a high risk of obsolescence. We take a gamble when we buy a new camcorder, VCR or TV – a new, better model could be round the corner.

All of those of you who remember the demise of Betamax and 8-track cartridges will be particularly worried about new formats making the tapes we use obsolete. Fortunately, the impact of a format war in the camcorder world has less effect than it did with VCRs or tape decks. Camcorders are not used primarily to play pre-recorded tapes – so shops do not have to carry thousands of different tapes for a number of formats. All you need for your camcorder is blank tape. There is little problem with shops, therefore, carrying half a dozen types of tape.

However, it is undoubtedly true that the formats that we use today have a limited life span. The big change will be the popularization of digital video. Just as CDs are changing the way we listen to music, so digital video will gradually replace the analogue systems we now use.

The one great advantage of digital video will be when it comes to editing and copying tapes. Digital signals are very resistant to degradation – and, theoretically at least, you could make a thousandth-generation copy of your original footage and still have a great picture. With current analogue tapes the picture and sound start to degrade with even a second-generation copy.

The difficulty with digital video is that the amount of information that has to be stored is immense. When you consider that every TV picture is made up of hundreds of thousands of picture elements, and that these are scanned at a rate of 25 per second in the UK and 30 in the USA, and that there are 3,600 seconds in an hour, it is easy to see what a colossal memory capacity is required.

A camcorder is capable of processing and recording 11 million pieces of signal information every second – and can keep on recording at this rate for several hours. Most computers could not sustain having to store this amount of information for long.

The answer to turning a video signal into digital data therefore lies in compression. To put it simply the signals are written in an electronic shorthand – some of the information is left out – and the rest is written down in a simplified form.

There are a number of compression systems used today which can keep the amount of information that has to be recorded down to a manageable size. These have been used for a number of years in computer applications, CD formats and professional video. Some of the standards used compress each frame separately, looking for similarities in each picture and simplifying it. Others use a more complicated process which compares a sequence of frames to look at duplicated information – this means the signal is compressed more, but can be restored with much more detail.

The first consumer digital camcorders coming onto the market use ¼-inch tape to record on. This Digital Video Cassette (DVC) format is housed in two different shell sizes – the one designed for camcorder use giving you tapes that

are little bigger than dictaphone cassettes. Digital camcorders could, therefore, be made much smaller than today's palm-sized models.

But other formats that use discs, or even solid state chips, for storage will come. At present, tape is used in that it gives a very large surface area to pack all the information into. But the advantage of getting away from tape is that you need fewer moving parts and simpler motors (or no motors at all). This should, eventually, mean cheaper and more reliable camcorders – although not until some time in the 21st century.

Before then, we will start to use video recorders that employ a relative of the compact disc to play and record the latest blockbuster films, and our favourite soaps. Machines that can play pre-recorded movies from CDs have been around for a while.

Tomorrow's televisions
The main stumbling block to the wholesale adoption of digital video is television itself. The TVs we currently use are firmly rooted in the analogue era. Unfortunately, in some respects, television technology does not move fast. There are too many existing users in the world for wholesale changes to happen overnight. Also, television is heavily dependent on broadcasting companies which are often directly answerable to governments. So, even decisions on which new technologies to pursue can take a long time.

High-definition television (HDTV) has been talked about for years. This would have been an analogue system that gave a dramatic improvement in picture quality, thanks to a doubling of the number of scanning lines. The system actually went on sale in Japan, under the name of HiVision.

However, whilst other countries have debated and argued about HDTV, digital video technologies have been improving all the time. It is now generally thought that the high-definition sets that we will watch next century will therefore use a digital system.

Whatever the future of television, one thing is (almost) certain. The new generation of TVs will be a different shape from the ones of today. They will be widescreen – with an aspect ratio of 16:9 (16 units wide by 9 units high); current sets use an aspect ration of 4:3. In fact, widescreen televisions have been on sale for a number of years already, and are particularly useful for watching feature films, which without exception are recorded in a widescreen format (though normally in a wider ratio than 16:9). However, as very few programmes are broadcast in this way, only a few of these analogue 'low-definition' widescreen sets have been sold to date.

A further trend is for television sets to become

thinner. LCD (liquid crystal display) sets have for the last few years been used for small-screen applications – for travel televisions, for camcorder viewfinders and portable computers. But Japanese manufacturers are continually making larger and larger LCD sets, which could eventually be cheap enough for use in our living rooms. Imagine being able to hang your television on the wall like a picture – rather than having a heavy cathode ray tube set taking over the corner of your room.

Another technology currently being explored in the search for thinner TVs is beam matrix displays. Here the picture is created in a similar way to that of traditional TVs, in that a fluorescent surface is illuminated with electrons. Because of this beam matrix, displays are as bright as current TVs and, unlike LCD screens, have less visible pixellation. Unlike a standard set, however, Flat Vision uses electrostatic deflection instead of magnetic deflection to control the electron beams. It divides the screen into thousands of unit screens, each with its own electron source. The early versions of these sets, which are on sale in Japan, are around a third of the depth of a similarly sized conventional set.

Digital editing

If there is one area of video that is racing ahead faster than any other, it has to be the integration of computers with video. Anyone who is familiar with current computer hardware will have seen the change. CD-Rom drives that allow you to play multimedia discs that combine sound, video and graphics on screen are now a standard feature on many computers. Boards that allow you to display live television pictures on your screen are now also packaged in computer kits.

The most useful result of this melding of technologies, as far as the camcorder enthusiast is concerned, has been in post-production. In the chapter on editing, we looked briefly at how the computer can help with graphics, titles and special effects. But the most exciting development has been in the ability to edit digitally.

The advantage of digital editing is that the cutting process can be done in a non-linear fashion. With traditional methods, you copy from one tape to another – and you have to put down the first shot of your final video before the second; at the very least, you must leave a gap of the right length for the first shot. With digital editing you don't have to do this. You can edit the second shot, move on to the fifth, go back to the third, do the closing credits and then return to fill in the other sections when you want to.

This ability to edit in a random order was one of cine film's strongest advantages. If you wanted to add another shot in the middle of your finished film you just spliced it in – and every-

thing that followed shunted along. This just isn't possible with normal video editing. To add something in the middle, you have to record over something you've already finished. In short, you practically have to start again.

Digital, or non-linear, editing has been available to professional videomakers for a number of years. Only more recently has the price of this technology started to come down. Soon it will be cheap enough for everyone to use.

The way that it works, as far as the consumer is concerned, is that the computer is fitted with a special board that turns incoming video footage into digital footage – using one of the compression systems mentioned above. Sections of this tape can then be recorded directly onto the computer's hard disc (or onto another storage device).

Using an appropriate editing software package, you can then edit the video as you like. These systems often also give you a wide range of digital effects such as wipes, dissolves and Chromakey – and you can often edit the soundtrack digitally as well. The finished video can then be played on the computer screen – or can be recorded back on to tape.

As hard drives with enough storage capacity, and processors which can handle data at super-high speeds, continue to improve and come down in price so digital editing will be available to a much larger market.

Once digital camcorders are widely available the mechanics for digital editing could be made even easier. All that the new camcorders would need is a digital AV out socket, as well as the analogue AV out socket it would need for replaying the tapes on television. This way the computer would only have to decompress the signal for on-screen display – it wouldn't have to digitally encode it in the first place.

We live in an exciting video age, and the sky does seem to be the limit for what the technicians can dream up to help us record pictures that move and speak. It's important, though, not to let the flashing lights on our machines dazzle us into believing that state-of-the-art technology is the be-all and end-all of video making.

It's good to have clear crisp pictures with vibrant colour and rich sound. It will be great if one day we can record our family epics onto a microchip the size of a fingernail. But as we've seen, making a good video still depends very much on human creativity and imagination. Without these skills all these electronic wonders are worthless.

Television Systems

Afghanistan	PAL	Kenya	PAL
Algeria	PAL	Kuwait	PAL
Argentina	PAL	Lebanon	SECAM
Australia	PAL	Libya	SECAM
Austria	PAL	Luxembourg	PAL/SECAM
Bahamas	NTSC	Malaysia	PAL
Bahrain	PAL	Malta	PAL
Bangladesh	PAL	Mexico	NTSC
Barbados	NTSC	Morocco	SECAM
Belgium	PAL	Netherlands	PAL
Bermuda	NTSC	New Zealand	PAL
Bolivia	NTSC	Nicaragua	NTSC
Brazil	PAL	Nigeria	PAL
Bulgaria	SECAM	North Korea	SECAM
Burma (Myanmar)	NTSC	Norway	PAL
Cambodia	PAL	Oman	PAL
Canada	NTSC	Pakistan	PAL
Chile	NTSC	Panama	NTSC
China	PAL	Paraguay	PAL
Cyprus	PAL/SECAM	Peru	NTSC
Denmark	PAL	Philippines	NTSC
Ecuador	NTSC	Poland	PAL
Egypt	SECAM	Portugal	PAL
El Salvador	NTSC	Puerto Rico	PAL
Ethiopia	PAL	Romania	SECAM
Fiji	PAL	Russia	SECAM
Finland	PAL	Saudi Arabia	SECAM
France	SECAM	Senegal	SECAM
French Guyana	SECAM	Singapore	PAL
Germany	PAL	South Africa	PAL
Ghana	PAL	South Korea	NTSC
Gibraltar	PAL	Spain	PAL
Greece	SECAM	Sri Lanka	PAL
Greenland	NTSC	Sweden	PAL
Guam	NTSC	Switzerland	PAL
Haiti	NTSC	Syria	SECAM
Honduras	NTSC	Tahiti	SECAM
Hong Kong	PAL	Taiwan	NTSC
Hungary	PAL	Tanzania	PAL
Iceland	PAL	Thailand	PAL
India	PAL	Trinidad	NTSC
Indonesia	PAL	Tunisia	SECAM
Iran	SECAM	Turkey	PAL
Iraq	SECAM	USA	NTSC
Ireland	PAL	Venezuela	NTSC
Israel	PAL	Vietnam	NTSC
Italy	PAL	Former Yugoslavia	PAL
Jamaica	NTSC	Zaire	SECAM
Japan	NTSC	Zambia	PAL
Jordan	PAL	Zimbabwe	PAL

Glossary

A

Aerial socket
Socket on a television that receives high-frequency signals picked up by aerial. Can be used as an input for replaying or copying camcorder footage if an RF adaptor is used, although the picture quality is lower than when using a direct AV connection.

Aperture
The adjustable opening in a lens which controls the amount of light passing into the camcorder. It also has a direct effect over depth of field.

Aspect ratio
The relationship between the width and the height of a picture.

Assemble editing
A method of editing where sequences are re-recorded, from one tape to another, in which shots are arranged in sequence, one after another.

Audio dub
An editing method where one of the sound tracks on the video tape is replaced without affecting the picture. Only possible on some camcorders and VCRs.

Audio in
The socket on a video recorder which receives an audio signal.

Audio mixer
A device which allows several audio signals to be laid down on a single track. Audio levels and quality can be adjusted in the process.

Autofocus (AF)
An electronic system for automatically focusing the camcorder's lens so that the main part of the picture appears sharp.

Automatic exposure (AE)
A system that automatically controls the iris (and sometimes gain and shutter-speed settings too) on a camcorder to ensure that the picture is not too bright or too dark.

Automatic gain control (AGC)
Circuits within a camcorder which automatically adjust the incoming video and/or audio signals to determined levels.

Auto white balance (AWB)
Camcorder system that adjusts the colour of the video picture to look normal to the human eye in any given lighting condition.

AV (audio/video)
Any component that handles both sound and video pictures.

Available light
The prevailing light in any scene – sunlight or domestic lighting in interiors.

B

Background
The furthermost plane in any shot, behind the main subject of the shot.

Backlight
A light source positioned behind the subject.

Backlight compensation (BLC)
Control on camcorder which increases the amount of exposure given to the picture. Used in backlight situations, to prevent subjects becoming silhouettes.

Barn doors
Metal flaps that are attached in front of a lamp, which can be adjusted to illuminate a scene selectively.

BCU (big close-up)
A shot in which the subject's face fills the screen.

Betamax
A tape format developed in the 1970s, which was eclipsed by VHS and is no longer in production.

Blacked tape
Video tape that has been recorded on with a totally black picture. It gives a professional look to the beginning and end of your video, and adds a sync signal for use when insert editing.

Boom
A long pole used to mount microphones above characters in a scene so that the microphone is close to the subject but is hidden from shot.

Bounced light
A light source reflected off surrounding walls or ceiling before it falls upon the subject.

C

Camcorder
A video camera and recorder housed in one portable unit.

Cardioid
Term which describes the heart-shaped pick-up zone of some microphones.

Character generator
A device built into some camcorders for creating titles over your video footage.

Charge-coupled device (CCD)
A photoconductive semi-conductor chip which is responsive to light of different wavelengths. It generates the electronic video signal in many video cameras and camcorders.

Chromakey
Term often used for colour separation overlay. In fact, a trade name.

Close down
To close the aperture down and thus reduce the amount of light passing through the lens.

Colour balance
Another name for white balance.

Colour separation overlay (CSO)
An electronic system by which two images can be combined, so that the first scene appears to have the second as background. Also known as Chromakey.

Colour temperature
Measurement of the colour of light. The human visual system adjusts for colour temperature all the time without us noticing. On a camcorder the automatic white balance system performs the same adjustment. Often measured in Kelvin (K).

Component video
A video signal where the brightness (luminance) and colour (chrominance) parts of the picture are separated. Found in high-band video formats such as Hi8 and S-VHS.

Composite video
The opposite to component video – a video signal where the brightness and colour are combined. Used by low-band video formats.

Contrast ratio
The range of brightness between the lightest and darkest areas in any scene.

Control-L
Remote-control socket found on some camcorders and VCRs that is mainly used in editing for controlling tape transport with an edit controller. Can also be used to control over camcorder functions, such as zooming.

Control track
The track of signal pulses along the length of a video tape which acts to control the speed of replay and help synchronize the video heads with the individual tracks on the tape.

Cookie
Slang term for a cucaloris, a device placed in front of a lamp to give a broken shadow effect to a scene.

Coverage
The shots required to convey fully the subject being recorded. Also, the shots required to allow continuity to be maintained.

Crab
A camera movement sideways across the action being recorded.

Crash zoom
Switching rapidly from wide angle to telephoto on the zoom lens, or vice versa, whilst recording.

Crossing the line
Moving the camera from one side of the action to the other. This can disrupt the audience's understanding of the spatial relationships displayed on the screen.

Crosslighting
A lighting arrangement using key- and fill-lights of equal luminance.

CRT (cathode ray tube)
The type of picture tube used in most television sets, and for black-and-white electronic view-finders on camcorders.

CU (Close-up)
Shot taken at short range from the camera. With people, a shot framed at head and shoulders.

Cut
An instantaneous change from one shot to another.

Cutaway
A shot within a sequence that is not central to the main action, but which adds additional information for the audience to absorb. A shot used whilst shooting or editing to separate two very similar shots, or to create a visual break.

D

Decibel (dB)
A logarithmic measurement for comparing different power levels in a signal. A doubling of power level is equivalent to 3dB, a thousandfold increase represents 60dB. Used in the measurement of signal-to-noise ratio, sound volume, sensitivity of microphones, and so on.

Denouement
The climax, or ending of a story.

Depth of field
The range of distances in which objects in a scene are in acceptably sharp focus. Depth of field varies with aperture size, subject distance and focal length.

Dew sensor
A detection device that shuts down the camcorder when it detects moisture. This stops the tape sticking to the recording heads and causing damage to the tape.

Digital
A signal which has been encoded as a series of ones and noughts. Digital technology is used in processing the picture signal in many camcorders, but is only used for recording the video signal in some, mainly professional, machines.

Digital effects
A range of effects which is possible when the video signal is processed digitally (see Digital). Effects possible include: mixes, slow shutter speeds, wipes, electronic zooms, timebase correctors and image stabilizers.

Discharger
Device that ensures that a rechargeable battery's voltage is reduced to an ideal level before recharging. This helps prolong the working life and optimum performance of the battery.

Dissolve
To change from one shot to another by gradually fading out the first and fading in the second.

Dolly
A camera mount on wheels which allows a smooth tracking action.

Draft
An early version of a script.

Drop out
Imperfection or particle of dust on a video tape that manifests itself as a black or white speck when the tape is played on a TV screen.

E

Edit controller
A unit that allows you to control both source deck and record deck during editing.

Edit deck
The deck on which the edited tape is created.

Edit script
A document identifying the points at which cuts should be made on the tapes to be edited.

Electromagnetic spectrum
The entire range of electromagnetic radiation, both visible and invisible.

Electronic viewfinder (EVF)
A small TV monitor which displays the image seen by the camera electronically, rather than optically. Can be either a black-and-white cathode ray tube, or a colour LCD screen.

Establishing shot
A shot which provides the audience with basic information: where the action is taking place, and who are the main characters. Also called an establisher.

Eyeline
The direction of gaze of a person shown in a scene.

F

Fill-light
The light used in a three-point lighting arrangement to lift the shadows caused by the key-light.

Filters
Translucent glass or plastic devices used to modify the quality of the light received by the camera. Some filters remove glare, others add distinctive colours to a scene. Some turn points of light into star shapes, whilst others use prisms to give a multiple image of the subject.

Flags
Used in lighting to block part of the light from a lamp.

Flat lighting
Lighting in which the subject is not readily lifted from the background due to lack of contrast.

Floods
Lights which produce a wide, evenly dispersed spread of illumination over a scene.

Flying erase head
Special head found on most camcorders and some VCRs that allows the exact amount of video to be erased, just before another shot is recorded on this section of tape. Far preferable to a fixed erase head.

FM audio
Soundtrack recorded beneath the video track using the helical scan system. It gives hi-fi sound quality. Either mono or stereo.

Focal length
Measurement of the magnification and angle of view of a given lens setting, generally stated in millimetres.

Focus
To adjust the lens so that the image is sharply delineated.

Follow focus
To adjust the focus, while shooting, so that a moving subject is always kept sharp.

Follow space
The area behind a subject when moving across the screen.

Foreground
The area in the shot in front of the main subject.

Frame
The area in which the image is presented: the TV screen. Also used to describe the act of placing subjects in shot in an aesthetically pleasing way.

G

Gel
Gelatin, often used as a filter on lights, windows or in front of the camcorder.

Generation
Each successive copy of a tape is called a generation – the original camcorder tape is the first generation, the edited tape of this on VHS is second generation, and a copy made of this is the third generation. The picture and sound quality deteriorate from one generation to the next.

Genlock
A device that allows computer graphics to be superimposed on a video tape.

Gun mic
A highly directional microphone.

H

Headroom
The screen space above a subject's head.

Helical scan
Recording system used on all camcorder and VCRs which writes the picture signal in diagonal strips along the moving tape using a recording head mounted on a rotating drum which is placed at an angle to the tape.

Hi8
High-band version of the 8mm/Video 8 camcorder format which records brightness and chrominance separately on special tape to give a high-quality picture with a horizontal resolution of up to 400 lines.

Hi-Fi (high fidelity)
A high-quality sound system (stereo or mono) which has a frequency response range of 20–20,000Hz.

High angle
A shot taken from a position in which the camera looks down on the subject.

High band
Any video format with a superior picture quality – ie Hi8, S-VHS and S-VHS-C.

I

Insert editing
An editing method in which video material is electronically inserted into an existing recording without affecting the mono, linear sound track.

Iris
The diaphragm in the lens, which regulates the intensity of the light entering the camera.

J

Jump cut
A cut between two shots where the subject appears to jump position for no obvious reason. Generally caused by starting to record again without changing camera angle and shot size. Normally to be avoided whenever possible.

K

Kelvin
Unit used for measuring colour temperature.

Key-light
The major component in a three-point lighting arrangement, illuminating the subject from the front.

L

Lavalier
A small microphone, often worn around the neck on a cord.

LCD (liquid crystal display)
Type of information display panel. Colour LCD panels are often used as alternatives to the traditional black-and-white CRT viewfinder on camcorders.

Lead space
The area in front of a person moving in a shot.

Level
The overall strength of an audio or video signal.

Logging
The act of listing the contents of a video tape prior to editing.

Long-shot
A shot which contains, at its closest, a complete human figure.

Low angle
A shot in which the camera shoots upwards at the subject from a position below it.

Lux
A unit measuring light intensity in a scene.

M

Macro
Feature on a camcorder for shooting very close to a subject, so that the subject appears larger than lifesize when the tape is replayed on a TV.

Master
The final version of a tape.

Master shot
A shot covering the major element of the action being conveyed.

Matte
A mask which cuts out part of the frame in order to achieve a special effect. Can be electronic or physical.

Matte box
A device attached to the end of the camera lens, to hold mattes.

Metal evaporated
The highest grade of tape for Hi8 camcorders.

Metal oxide
The kind of tape used by camcorders and VCRs in the VHS family (ie VHS, VHS-C, S-VHS and S-VHS-C formats).

Metal particle
Tape used by 8mm and Hi8 camcorders.

Mid-shot
A shot containing the human figure framed just above the waist level.

Monitor
A TV connected directly to a video camera or VCR, to allow the video output to be checked.

N

Narrative
The unfolding of a story that takes place through changes in the plot.

Nicad (nickel-cadmium)
A common type of rechargeable battery used in camcorders. Other types found include lead acid, nickel metal hydride, and lithium ion.

Noise
Unwanted electronic disturbance to the video signal.

NTSC
Acronym of the National Television Standards Committee. The television system employed in the USA and Japan, as well as other countries.

O

On camera
In a position in front of the camera so as to be visible in a shot.

Open up
To increase the aperture and thus allow more light into the camera.

Out of shot
Not seen by the camera.

P

PAL
Acronym for Phase Alternation Line, the television system used in most of Europe (but not France).

Pan
A horizontal movement of the camera on its mount, taking in new areas of a scene.

PCM
Digital hi-fi stereo sound-recording system used on a few Hi8 camcorders. Used in addition to hi-fi FM tracks, and can be audio dubbed.

Photoflood
The basic type of light, commonly called a flood. It illuminates a wide area.

Pick-up tube
In old cameras, the part of the camera which converted light into the electronic video signal. The CCD does the same thing in today's models.

Pixel
An abbreviation for picture element. A single light-sensitive cell in a CCD image chip. Each chip can have half a million of these elements. Also the individual picture element of an LCD screen.

Playback deck
When editing, the deck which plays the original tape to be edited. Also called the source deck.

Point of view
A shot in which the camera takes up a character's position in order to reveal to the audience what he or she sees.

Props
The objects apparent in a shot.

Pull focus
A technique in which focus moves from one plane to another as the shot progresses. This technique is also known as throw-focus.

Q

Quartz-lighting
High-intensity lighting which uses quartz halogen bulbs.

R

RCTC
Abbreviation for Rewritable Consumer Timecode. Timecode system found on some Hi8 camcorders. Has the advantage over VITC in that it can be recorded separately from the picture.

Rehearse and record
A production technique in studios in which segments of a programme are rehearsed and then recorded before proceeding to the next part of the show.

Research
The gathering of information and visual materials before beginning a production.

RF adaptor
Device that converts composite AV signals from a camcorder into radio frequencies which can then be input into the aerial socket of a television or VCR.

Rig in
To set up lights, sound equipment and cameras before shooting begins.

Rim light
The halo effect caused by backlighting on a subject. Can be more or less pronounced according to the light's intensity.

Rough cut
The early stages of the editing process from which the final edit emerges.

S

Saturation
The intensity of colour in an image.

Scart
21-pin AV in/out socket widely used on TVs, VCRs and edit equipment.

Scoop
A large floodlight.

Scrim
Gauze placed in front of a light source to diffuse the light falling on a scene.

Script
A detailed description of the production to be recorded, including camera angles and shot descriptions.

SECAM
Acronym for Séquenciel Couleur à Mémoire, the television system used in France and elsewhere.

Sequence
A discrete part of a narrative, usually with its own recognizable beginning and end.

SFX
Abbreviation for special effects.

Shoot
To operate the camera.

Shot
The material recorded by the camera in a single operation. Also the image seen by the camera.

Source deck
The deck used to replay original material when editing.

Special effects
Illusions created either during shooting or added electronically during the editing stage.

Special effects generator (SEG)
A unit which allows the electronic manipulation of the video signal during editing in order to create a range of special effects.

Spots
Lights which produce an intense, concentrated beam.

Still
A single photographic image.

Storyboard
A detailed drawing of the sequence of shots to be taken during coverage of an event or story.

Supercardioid
Shotgun microphone with an angle of acceptance of around 120 degrees.

S-VHS
High-band version of the VHS tape format that records brightness and colour separately on special tape to give a high-quality picture with a horizontal resolution of up to 400 lines.

S-VHS-C
High-band version of the VHS-C tape format – or compact version of the S-VHS format, depending on how you want to look at it!

Switching
To switch from one electronic source to another.

T

Talent
Professional term for performers.

Telecine
A system for transferring film or slide material on to videotape. This usually involves projecting the film on to a specially designed screen and recording the result with a video camera.

Telephoto lens
A lens of long focal length which gives an enlarged image of a distant scene. Also the longer focal lengths available on a zoom lens.

Three-point lighting
The standard lighting system used in artificially lit scenes. It consists of backlight, key-light and fill-light.

Three-shot
A shot in which three people are shown within the frame.

Throw focus
The same as pull focus.

Tilt
A vertical movement, up or down, of the camera on its mount.

Time code
A frame-by-frame time reference recorded on videotape. Used when extreme accuracy is needed when editing. Common types of time code used on enthusiast camcorders include VITC and RCTC.

Track
A movement of the camera parallel to the action.

Treatment
A brief outline of a proposed story or programme.

Tripod
An adjustable three-legged camera mount with a head allowing pan and tilt movements of the camera.

TTL
Abbreviation for through the lens – used to describe focusing, exposure and white balance systems that take their readings this way.

Two-shot
A shot which shows two people in the frame.

U

U-Matic
A semi-professional ¾ inch videotape format.

V

VCR
A video cassette recorder.

VHS
Standing for Video Home System, the dominant domestic video cassette recorder format, pioneered by JVC.

VHS-C
Compact version of VHS, which can be played back on a VHS machine using an adaptor.

Video 8 or 8mm
Low-band tape format specifically developed for use in camcorders. As the tape is much narrower than that used by the VHS formats, a special type of tape (metal particle) is needed for the system to be able to store the information that is needed to describe each frame of video. Pioneered by Sony.

Videotape
A plastic-based material with a metallic coating on which the video signal is recorded as a series of magnetic stripes.

Viewfinder
An optical or electronic device allowing the image seen by the camera to be monitored.

Vision mixer
A post-production accessory that allows you to mix two different video signals together so that one gradually fades into the other.

VITC
Abbreviation for vertical interval time code. Time code system used on some VHS-family camcorders.

Voice-over
A commentary heard by the audience without the speaker being in shot. Often used in documentary work.

VU meter
Volume Unit meter, a device which measures and displays the relative loudness of an audio signal. Used to help balance sound levels during recording.

W

Wavelength
The distance from one point in a given wave to a corresponding point on the next cycle. Light of differing wavelengths is perceived by the camcorder to be of different colours, the human brain compensates for this automatically. Hence the need for white balance systems.

Whip pan
A rapid pan movement of the camera so as to create a deliberately blurred image.

White balance
The system for determining true colour values on a video camera.

Wide-angle lens
A lens with a short focal length which gives a large angle of view. Also the shorter focal lengths available on the zoom lens.

Wildtrack
Background sound recorded separately from the video picture whilst out on location. Can be recorded on a separate audio tape recorder, or with your camcorder. Used for audio dubbing at the post-production stage.

Wind gag
Acoustic foam placed around a microphone to reduce wind noise on outdoor locations.

Wipe
A special effect in which one image gradually replaces another on screen.

Y

Y/C signal
Component video signal (Y stands for luminance, and C for chrominance).

Z

Zoom lens
A lens of continuously variable focal length, and therefore variable angle of view.

Zoom ratio
The ratio between the longest and shortest focal lengths on a camcorder's zoom. A camcorder with a 6–72mm zoom is said to have a 12:1, or 12x, zoom ratio.

INDEX
AND
ACKNOWLEDGMENTS

INDEX

ACKNOWLEDGMENTS

The publishers would like to thank the following organizations for their kind co-operation in supplying photographs or video equipment for photography:

Panasonic Consumer Electronics UK
Panasonic House, Willoughby Road, Bracknell, Berkshire RG12 8FP.

Sharp UK
Thorp Road, Newton Heath, Manchester M10 9BE.

Keith Johnson & Pelling Ltd
Promandis House, Bradbourne Drive, Tilbrook, Milton Keynes MK7 8AJ.

Canon UK, Photographic Division,
Brent Trading Centre, North Circular Road, Neasden, London NW10.

Sangers, Priory House, Pitsford St, Birmingham B18 6LX.

Sony UK, The Heights, Brooklands, Weybridge, Surrey.

Bandridge, 18 Deerpark Road, Wimbledon, London SW19 3YU.

Video Camera magazine, WV Publications, 57-59 Rochester Place, London NW1 9JU.

The photography on pages 62, 63, 68–69, 70, 71, 72, 73 and 74 was made possible through the kind permission of the following:

Le Vuairneige Hôtel, Verchaix, France (62); Hôtel Le Parc, Near Beaune, France (63, pictures 5 and 6); Simon Whyte (sponsored by Santa Cruz & Oakley), and The Avalanche Club and friends, Flaine, France (68–69); Trewithen Gardens, Cornwall, UK (70); Queluz Palace, Lisbon, Portugal (71, pictures 2 and 3); Ganna Walska Lotusland, Santa Barbara, USA (71, pictures 4 and 5); Tresco Gardens, Scilly Isles, UK (72, top); The Huntington Gardens Administration, Los Angeles, USA (72, bottom); Giverny, France (73, top); The White House, Connecticut, USA (73, bottom); Ray Woodcock (74, picture 1).

The map on pages 164–65 is reproduced with the permission of Michelin from their *Motoring Atlas of France*.

Additional Photography:
Equipment: Andrew Hayward
People & Places: Sally and Richard Greenhill

All other photography is by John Hedgecoe except on the following pages and as indicated: 10–11, ET Archive; 25, 45 (top) Octopus Books Limited; 45 (right) and 165 (bottom), Tony Stone Worldwide; 48, 52–53, Templar Publishing Limited; 134 Wisniewski/ZEFA; 136 (top and bottom), Claude Nuridsany and Marie Perenou/ Science Photo Library; 137 (top, middle and bottom), Dr Jeremy Burgess/Science Photo Library; 138–39, 165 (top and middle), ZEFA; 234–35, John Cole/Impact Photos.